About the author

Sidney Joseph Perelman (1904–1979) was born into a Russian Jewish immigrant family in Brooklyn. He grew up in Providence, Rhode Island and attended Brown University in 1922 where he became the cartoonist of the college magazine and finally its editor. After publishing his first two books, he was invited to Hollywood by Groucho Marx to script two films: *Monkey Business* and *Horse Feathers*. It was an unhappy experience and Perelman soon went back East, though he would return again and again to work for the studios and eventually won an Oscar in 1956 for *Around the World in Eighty Days*. A regular contributor to the *New Yorker* from 1935, he soon became the magazine's most successful humorist. He continued in this vein for the next thirty years writing scenarios, sketches, plays, travel pieces and publishing twenty books – many of them collections of his *New Yorker* pieces. He divided his time between New York and his country home in Erwinna, Bucks County, Pennsylvania. In his later years he travelled the globe, settling briefly in England, before finally returning to New York where he died aged 75.

The World of
S J Perelman

PRION HUMOUR CLASSICS

* for copyright reasons these titles are not available in the USA or Canada in the Prion edition.

The World
of
S J Perelman

with a new introduction by
WOODY ALLEN

PRION

This collection published 2000
First published in paperback 2006 by Prion

an imprint of the Carlton Publishing Group
20 Mortimer Street
London W1T 3JW

Stories in this collection are taken from:
Crazy Like a Fox © 1944
Keep it Crisp © 1947
The Road to Miltown © 1957
The Rising Gorge © 1961
Baby It's Cold Inside © 1970
All copyright © SJ Perelman

Introduction copyright © Woody Allen 2000

A catalogue record for this book is available from
the British Library.

ISBN 978-1-85375-594-1

Jacket illustration by David Hitch

Printed in Great Britain by CPI Group (UK) Ltd, Croydon CR0 4YY

Contents

Introduction

by WOODY ALLEN

There is no writer of comic prose to compare with S J Perelman. It is really as simple as that. His writing towers above Robert Benchley's who was the other truly great and authentic funny author and is his closest competitor. Lardner, Ade, Bill Nye, Leacock and Thurber were often superb, yet none holds a candle to the creator of Lucas Membrane, the Wormsers, Suppositorsky and "I Am Not Nor Have I Ever Been A Matrix of Lean Meat", among other inspired flights. No one writing today touches Perelman's comic flair, his inventive lunacy, his erudite narrative skill, and dazzlingly original dialogue.

No collection can do him justice because his humor is so inventive and varied that inevitably certain of one's favorite masterpieces get left out as choices must be made. Still no collection of his is ever less than wonderful because over the years there have been so many hilarious pieces to pick from. I usually prefer his later writing but that does not mean I don't often laugh out loud at the broader earlier gems. I began reading him in my teens and he has never disappointed me. Among all the comedy writers I've worked with or spoken to over the years, Perelman was always the most revered icon, the most widely-imitated comic genius and the most discouraging to any would-be funny prose stylist. For many of us, starting out years ago, it was impossible to not write like him, so dominating was his elegant voice.

This collection, I am sure, will demonstrate that I have not given him too big a build-up.

EDITOR'S NOTE

After serving a comic apprenticeship at *Judge* magazine and on his college rag before that, S J Perelman had his first piece accepted by the *New Yorker* in 1930 at the age of 26. He went on to make it his spiritual home, becoming a regular contributor from 1935 until his death in 1979. Perelman enjoyed both the steady income and the creative freedom on offer at the *New Yorker* – his editor never tried to fiddle with his baroque prose or ask him to tone down his often obscure insider references. He was deeply frustrated throughout his career in his role elsewhere as a jobbing writer for both Hollywood and Broadway where he frequently felt his work was abused and misunderstood. His *New Yorker* comic essays or *feuilletons* as he called them, became the only form of writing which he truly relished. So meticulous was he, that his output rarely topped 1,000 words per week, despite the fact that he wrote six days a week from 10am to 6pm. He claimed to rewrite most of his pieces at least thirty times, retyping each version from scratch.

Most of the work gathered here first appeared in the pages of the *New Yorker* and occasionally in a variety of other magazines: *College Humour, Judge, Life, Contact, Stage, Holiday*. The present selection has been made from the regular collections of his essays that spanned his entire career: *Crazy Like a Fox* (1944) – a 'best of' his early material; *Keep It Crisp* (1947); *The Road to Miltown* (1957); *The Rising Gorge* (1961); *Baby It's Cold Inside* (1970). As such, it is the most comprehensive Perelman collection available to date.

AG

Beauty and the Bee

It is always something of a shock to approach a news-stand which handles trade publications and find the *Corset and Underwear Review* displayed next to the *American Bee Journal*. However, newsstands make strange bedfellows, as anyone who has ever slept with a newsstand can testify, and if you think about it at all (instead of sitting there in a torpor with your mouth half-open) you'd see this proximity is not only alpha-betical. Both the *Corset and Underwear Review* and the *American Bee Journal* are concerned with honeys; although I am beast enough to prefer a photograph of a succulent nymph in satin Lastex Girdleiere with Thrill Plus Bra to the most dramatic snapshot of an apiary, each has its place in my scheme.

The *Corset and Underwear Review*, which originates at the Haire Publishing Company, 1170 Broadway, New York City, is a magazine for jobbers. Whatever else a corset jobber is, he is certainly nobody's fool. The first seventy pages of the magazine comprise an album of superbly formed models posed in various attitudes of sweet surrender and sheathed in cunning artifices of whalebone, steel, and webbing. Some indication of what

1

S J Perelman

Milady uses to give herself a piquant front elevation may be had from the following list of goodies displayed at the Hotel McAlpin Corset Show, reported by the March, 1935, *Corset and Underwear Review*: "Flashes and Filmys, Speedies and Flexees, Sensations and Thrills, Snugfits and Even-Puls, Rite-Flex and Free-Flex, Smoothies and Silk-Skins, Imps and Teens, La Triques and Waikikis, Sis and Modern Miss, Sta-Downs and Props, Over-Tures and Reflections, Lilys and Irenes, Willo-th-wisps and Willoways, Miss Smartie and MisSimplicity, Princess Youth and Princess Chic, Miss Today and Soiree, Kordettes and Francettes, Paristyles and Rengo Belts, Vassarettes and Foundettes, Fans and Fade Aways, Beau Sveltes and Beau Formas, Madame Adrienne and Miss Typist, Stout-eze and Laceze, Symphony and Rhapsody, Naturade and Her Secret, Rollees and Twin Tops, Charma and V-Ette, La Camille and La Tec."

My neck, ordinarily an alabaster column, began to turn a dull red as I forged through the pages of the *Corset and Underwear Review* into the section called "Buyer News." Who but Sir John Suckling could have achieved the leering sensuality of a poem by Mrs. Adelle Mahone, San Francisco representative of the Hollywood–Maxwell Company, whom the magazine dubs "The Brassière Bard of the Bay District"?

Out-of-town buyers!—during your stay
At the McAlpin, see our new display.
There are bras for the young, support for the old,
Up here for the shy, down to there for the bold.
We'll have lace and nets and fabrics such as
Sturdy broadcloths and satins luscious.

We'll gladly help your profits transform
If you'll come up to our room and watch us perform.
Our new numbers are right from the Coast:
Snappy and smart, wait!—we must not boast—
We'll just urge you to come and solicit your smiles,
So drop in and order your Hollywood styles.

One leaves the lacy *chinoiseries* of the *Corset and Underwear Review* with reluctance and turns to the bucolic *American Bee Journal*, published at Hamilton, Illinois, by C. P. Dadant. Here Sex is whittled down to a mere nubbin; everything is as clean as a whistle and as dull as a hoe. The bee is the *petit bourgeois* of the insect world, and his keeper is a self-sufficient stooge who needs and will get no introduction to you. The pages of the *American Bee Journal* are studded with cocky little essays like "Need of Better Methods of Controlling American Foulbrood" and "The Swarming Season in Manitoba." It is only in "The Editor's Answers," a query column conducted by Mr. Dadant, that Mr. Average Beekeeper removes his mask and permits us to peep at the warm, vibrant human beneath. The plight of the reader who signs himself "Illinois" (I've seen *that* name somewhere) is typical:

I would like to know the easiest way to get a swarm of bees which are lodged in between the walls of a house. The walls are of brick and they are in the dead-air space. They have been there for about three years. I would like to know method to use to get the bees, not concerned about the honey.

The editor dismisses the question with some claptrap about a "bee smoker" which is too ridiculous to repeat. The best bet I see for "Illinois" is to play upon the weakness of all bees. Take a small boy smeared with honey and lower him between the walls. The bees will fasten themselves to him by the hundreds and can be scraped off when he is pulled up, after which the boy can be thrown away. If no small boy smeared with honey can be found, it may be necessary to take an ordinary small boy and smear him, which should be a pleasure.

From the Blue Grass comes an even more perplexed letter:

I have been ordering a few queens every year and they are always sent as first-class mail and are thrown off the fast trains that pass here at a speed of 60 miles an hour. Do you think it does the queens any harm by throwing them off these fast trains? You know they get an awful jolt when they hit the ground. Some of these queens are very slow about doing anything after they are put in the hive. —KENTUCKY.

I have no desire to poach on George Washington Cable's domain, but if that isn't the furthest North in Southern gallantry known to man, I'll eat his collected works in Macy's window at high noon. It will interest every lover of chivalry to know that since the above letter was published, queen bees in the Blue Grass have been treated with new consideration by railroad officials. A Turkey-red carpet similar to that used by the Twentieth Century Limited is now unrolled as the train stops, and each queen, blushing to the very roots of her antennae, is escorted to her hive by a uniformed porter. The rousing strains of the cakewalk, the comical antics of the darkies, the hiss of fried chicken sputtering in the pan, all combine to make the scene unforgettable.

4

But the predicaments of both "Illinois" and "Kentucky" pale into insignificance beside the problem presented by another reader:

I have been asked to "talk on bees" at a nearby church some evening in the fall. Though I have kept bees for ten years, I am "scared stiff" because not a man in the audience knows a thing about bees and I am afraid of being too technical.

I plan to take along specimens of queen, drone and worker, also a glass observatory hive with bees, smoker and tools, an extra hive, and possibly some queen cell cups, etc.

Could you suggest any manipulating that might be done for the "edification of the audience"? I've seen pictures of stunts that have been worked, like making a beard of bees; and I've heard of throwing the bees out in a ball only to have them return to the hive without bothering anyone. But, I don't know how these stunts are done, nor do I know of any that I could do with safety. (I don't mind getting a sting or two myself, but I don't want anyone in the audience to get stung, or I might lose my audience.)

I've only opened hives a few times at night, but never liked the job as the bees seem to fly up into the light and sting very readily. That makes me wonder whether any manipulating can be done in a room at night.

How long before the affair would I need to have the bees in the room to have them settle down to the hive?—NEW YORK.

The only thing wrong with "New York" is that he just doesn't like bees. In one of those unbuttoned moods everybody has, a little giddy with cocoa and crullers, he allowed himself to be cajoled by the vestrymen, and now, face to face with his ordeal, he is sick with loathing for bees and vestrymen alike. There is one solution, however, and that is for "New York" to wrap himself tightly in muslin the night of the lecture and stay in bed with his hat on. If the vestrymen come for him, let him throw the bees out in a ball. To hell with whether they return or not, and that goes for the vestrymen, too. It certainly goes for me. If I ever see the postman trudging toward my house with a copy of the *American Bee Journal*, I'm going to lodge myself in the dead-air space between the walls and no amount of small boys smeared with honey will ever get me out. And you be careful, *American Bee Journal*—I *bite*.

Abby,
This is Your Father

A certain five-cent weekly published in Philadelphia with a sworn circulation of 3,100,000 has been given lately to a good deal of blushing and stammering and other signs of pretty confusion. Naturally I cannot violate professional ethics by using real names, but, spelled backward, the legend on the magazine runs "Tsop Gnineve Yadrutas Eht" (a catchy enough title for any reader's money), and it was founded Anno Domini 1728 by Beljamir Flankler. I fope I mek misef clirr.

The reason for all this dimpling and coloring up to the roots of the hair is something the editors are modest enough to term "Post Luck." On a number of occasions their articles have been so timely as to seem almost clairvoyant. For example, a biography of Will Rogers had barely concluded before his death was announced, and similarly General Walter Krivitsky, *geboren* Schmelka Ginzberg, forecast the Russo-German nuptials at a time when the happy couple was still issuing denials to friends and relatives. Whatever the mysterious pipeline it possesses to the infinite, the *Post* is constantly hiring the back page of the *New York Times* to kiss its reflection in the mirror and murmur,

"Oo, you pitty sing." Throughout which, of course, *Collier's* waspishly pats its back hair into place and pretends to be looking the other way. But not long ago, baker-fresh from the editorial oven and as if to confound the skeptics, there came another startling proof of the *Post*'s telepathy. The place of honor in one of the late autumn issues was given over to the opening installment of *Mary, This Is Your Mother*, by Catherine Hayes Brown, subheaded "The Unique Story of Helen Hayes, as Told by Her Mother." Now hold your hats. Less than a month before that, *Ladies and Gentlemen*, a new play by Charles MacArthur and Ben Hecht, opened in New York, and in its leading rôle was *Helen Hayes*! Why, it's enough to make a body's flesh creep.

The epistolary form is a mold sanctified in the editorial rooms of the *Post*, where it is still remembered that George Horace Lorimer, the Great White Father of the Curtis publications, made a sizable bale of scratch out of a little book called *Letters of a Self-Made Merchant to His Son*. How many editions this early classic attained I do not know, but the last time I wandered down Fourth Avenue it still covered the second-hand bookstores like a mulch. The tradition was subsequently carried forward in the pages of the *Post* by William Hazlett Upson with his letters of a tractor salesman, and now, as the torch drops from his nerve-less hand, Mrs. Brown picks it up with *Mary, This Is Your Mother*. To me, it seems a rather roundabout way of telling a child about its mother to write it letters in a magazine which costs a nickel, when you can deal out a few crisp facts right in the kitchen, but I suppose it cuts down the back talk considerably.

As if this whole affair were not spooky enough already, the very week Mrs. Brown began her revelations the present writer's mother was on the verge of publishing some letters dealing with his career which she had written to her granddaughter. They reveal an astonishing parallel to Mrs. Brown's letters and one that should prove interesting to all lovers of good clean parallels. In reading them, it is well to remember that many portions are in anapaestic pentameter, as they were intended to be sung through tissue paper stretched over a comb. No attempt has been made to edit the letters other than removing the checks they contained and cashing them.

ABBY DEAR:

I am going to write you a lot of letters about your daddy's early life, and you just try and stop me. And that goes for him too. And what's more, I'm going to get them printed if I have to do it on a hand press. A Mr. Caxton in the next block, who is very clever about such things, has just invented movable type, and he has promised to help me.

Enclosed is a little remembrance for your birthday. The green stones are what we call emeralds, the white sparkly ones diamonds. It costs about $585,000; it is not much to look at, but will do you for rainy days.

Lovingly,
GRANDMA

ABBY DEAR:

I suppose you often wonder what your daddy was like as a small boy. Well, he was just the most serious and sober little man you can imagine. He had a long, drooping Velvet Joe mustache, dipped snuff constantly, and was head bookkeeper for Portfolio & Dugdale, the corn factors. I don't think he ever really cared much about his wife, though he adored his children (he had three by the time he was seven years old). He was always moping around in a brown study, and when people spoke to him he would listen with only half an ear. To do him justice, that was all he had; the balance had been cropped for thievery, so you can see he had something to mope about.

When he was about eight, he stopped talking altogether, and I took him to Italy in an effort to revive his spirits. He spoke only once. We were floating along the Grand Canal in a gondola when a man attired as a Venetian nobleman of the fourteenth century lost his footing and toppled off the Bridge of Sighs. Your daddy smiled wanly and remarked to nobody in particular, "It shouldn't happen to a doge."

I know how fond you are of driving around these brisk autumn days, but you must see your pony doesn't catch cold. Wouldn't we feel awful if Toby dropped dead of pneumonia or something? I have had Jaeckel's stitch several chinchilla coats into a warm rug for him, and make sure he takes it off when he comes into the house.

Devotedly,
GRANDMA

ABBY DEAR:

By the time your daddy was eleven, he had made enough money to retire and give up all his time to translating the works of Elbert Hubbard, the Sage of Aurora, into Armenian, which he claimed would out-sell *The Trail of the Lonesome Pine*. Unfortunately, like all successful men, he had made a good many enemies in business, and when the book came out they went around talking against it, so it didn't do as well as some other books that year. Then his enemies started pounding him on Wall Street and brought on the panic of 1907, and your daddy lost every penny. It is to his credit that he sat down without a whimper and wrote *Bleak House, The*

Gilded Age, and a host of other successful novels which paid off every last creditor. But he was thirteen when he finished, and a man broken in health.

During your father's convalescence at Savin Rock, your Uncle Hosea—you remember, he was a famous oarsman at New Haven—came to visit us. As he alighted from the train, the Yale crew was having its annual banquet there and they recognized him. A cheer went up, and one of their number swung Uncle Hosea over his shoulder and bore him, kicking and screaming, through the streets. I was naturally alarmed at Hosea's tardiness in arriving, and expressed my anxiety. "We tried to keep it from you," remarked your daddy, "but poor Uncle Hosea was carried off by a stroke."

Under separate cover I am sending you an amusing keepsake, a string of pearls that once belonged to Maria Theresa of Austria. They are not in very good condition; however, you can knot the four strands together and use them for skipping rope.

Always,
GRANDMA

ABBY DEAR:

I know that the question uppermost in your mind is where your daddy spent the years between fifteen and twenty-one. The explanation he gives to the world is that although Moriarty lay at the bottom of the Reichenbach Fall, there still remained at large the second most dangerous man in London, Colonel Sebastian Moran. Until such time as Moran would show his hand, your daddy says he amused himself by traveling in Tibet, paying a short but interesting visit to the Khalifa at Khartoum (the results of which he communicated to the Foreign Office), and doing some research into the coal-tar derivatives at Montpellier. I may say that the whole story is a pack of lies.

The real facts are these. On his fifteenth birthday I took

your daddy to a matinée at the Apollo Burlesk and afterward to Schrafft's, where he had three mint smashes. On our way home we stopped in front of one of those shoddy auction rooms which line West Forty-second Street. The auctioneer exhibited a hideous brown jardinière and offered it to the first bidder. Next to us in the crowd stood a lady holding by the hand her child, who chanced to be a Siamese twin. Each of the twins wore on his head one of those aviator helmets so popular with children. "Just a moment," interposed your daddy loudly, "the pot goes to this lady here!" "Why?" scowled the auctioneer. "Because she's got a pair of aces back to back," returned your daddy. The crowd immediately rushed him and inflicted such damage that we were six years restoring his face to a condition where dogs no longer howled when they saw him.

Do you know where the Tebo Yacht Basin is, dear? Well, the next time you are in New York and find your hotel tiresome, tell the cab driver to take you over to Brooklyn and go aboard the *Corsair II*. I bought it for you from Mr. Morgan and it might be a lark to spend the night on your very own little boat. When you leave, don't forget to tell the captain to scuttle it, and oblige

Your ever-adoring
GRANDMA

Slow—Dangerous Foibles Ahead!

Some years ago, about the time Clayton, Jackson, and Durante were twisting you around their little finger at the Parody Club, there was a strange and shabby clip joint around the corner on West Forty-ninth Street. The patrons of this rookery were chiefly small, tight men who were understood to be on the lam, and a few Fordham undergraduates affecting an insolence found only at New Haven. The floor show consisted of a couple of refugees from the Orpheum circuit exchanging breezy cross-fire and flailing each other into insensibility. There was nothing at all exceptional about these two artists, but every now and again, on alternate Tuesdays, the straight man would pause in his routine and with studied ambiguity deliver a remark to his partner which mysteriously electrified a number of the customers. The expression ran, "The stuff is here —and it's mellow." Eventually one of the illuminati, whose name oddly enough happened to be Tony Illuminati, took pity on my bewilderment. He explained that a fresh shipment of happy dust had just arrived and might be purchased from the cigarette girl.

Well, the stuff is here again—and mellow it is

indeed. The editors of *Vogue*, ever quick to sniff out the trend and interpret the mode, recently called in nine important American industrial designers and asked them each to create a dress for the Woman of the Future in the World of Tomorrow. The boys spat on their hands—their own hands, not those of the editors of *Vogue*—and leapt to their T-squares. The results were run up by nine leading New York shops, photographed by nine leading photographers named Anton Bruehl, and appear on nine pages of the February issue. And in case you think there's nothing to numerology, Mummy has had a simply blinding headache for the past nine days.

After a hasty peek into their crystal ball, the designers were unanimous in the opinion that the Girl of Tomorrow would differ considerably from Miss 1943, who, it appears, is little better than a bundle of assorted neuroses, bronchitis, and stocking runs. "Medical Science will have made her body Perfect," fluently reports Mr. Donald Deskey. "She'll never know obesity, emaciation, colds in the head, superfluous hair, or a bad complexion—thanks to a controlled diet, controlled basal metabolism. Her height will be increased, her eyelashes lengthened—with some X-hormone." Lest this terrify you or remind you of Mr. Max Beerbohm's description of posterity in *Enoch Soames* ("...all of them smelling rather strongly of carbolic. And all of them quite hairless"), Mr. George Sakier adds a reassuring note: "The woman of the future will be tall and slim and lovely; she will be bred to it—for the delectation of the community and her own happiness. She will have a new freedom in time and space. She will move in a world of vast horizons. Her viewpoint will be clear and direct. She will be free from complexes and inhibitions. Her clothes will be simple and free from fantasy. She will take the miracles of science for granted, and will not make a fetish of functional forms, or of design-for-function." I breathed a little easier when I read that. Every time you ask your hostess at a party these days, "Who is that tall girl in the corner with the enchanting bosom?" you invariably get the careless reply, "Oh, that's Liane. She makes a fetish of functional forms and design-for-function." And as if this weren't bad enough, it always turns out Liane has a manic-depressive husband who makes a fetish of hitting people who tickle his wife.

Given this superb chassis, the designers seem evenly divided about upholstering it. Messrs. Teague, Sakier, Deskey, and Dreyfuss feel that the maximum of it will be put on display, and consequently package the Woman of Tomorrow in transparent chiffon, glass yarn, and cellophane; Mr. Dreyfuss, who, I take it, is a more old-fashioned type boy, favors a skin-tight black net, which was good enough for my grandfather and is good enough for me. "These materials," explains Mr. Teague of his fabrics of the future, "will be of chemical origin, and many will be either transparent or translucent, *with an individual life of their own*." I hope this last phrase of Mr. Teague's is purely figurative; offhand, the thought of clothes leading an existence independent of their owner is a little on the spooky side. How are you going to remain cool and poised on that future day when you demand hotly of your wife, "Where in the hell are those pants I threw over that chair last night?" only to get the answer, "Oh, they went up to Pride's Crossing for the weekend with my girdle. They'll be back Tuesday morning"?

The other camp among the designers—Messrs. Wright, Loewy, Arens, and Platt—is much more inclined to stress woman's age-old desire for fancy plumage. To this end they wrap her in aluminum foil, woollens interwoven with electric wire, and as yet undiscovered fabrics, to quote Mr. Loewy, "of microscopic cellular construction, made of a contracting and expanding fibre." What is this awful preoccupation with having your clothes twitch around in a horrid little life of their own? Did I miss something? I have the strange feeling that I have been asleep for twenty years and that everybody is jeering at my unkempt hair and rusty fowling piece.

When it comes to Milady's accessories, there is no holding back the boys; they just lay back on the hip and puff till the bunk is blue with smoke. "She may wear in her hair a headlight," says Mr. Wright of his model in evening dress, "an ornamental cylinder with a huge man-made diamond electrically lighted." The least her escort could do under the circumstances is carry an old-fashioned stem-winding watch and whistle at the grade crossings. Mr. Arens, dressing a hypothetical bride in glass, confines her waist in a sequin belt, of which he says, "These sequins are really 'Stimsonite' traffic reflectors of Lucite, made by the Signal Service Corporation. They are warranted to pick up and reflect the light from an automobile headlight a mile distant," which certainly ought to prove a boon to the innumerable brides who are members of the United States

Army Signal Corps. Mr. Dreyfuss provides his miss with a combination electric fan and vanity case, described as follows: "Nothing coquettish about it, for it will get its current by radio waves through the ether and will cool this girl, as well as clip the noses of any unwelcome suitors. The propeller-like blades, made of a transparent plastic, will fold into the interior, which is commodious enough to carry the eight million contraptions that crowd today's purses. (It was executed by Volupté.)" I trust I do not speak with bitterness, Mr. Dreyfuss, but to clothe a young lady in skin-tight black net and then hand her a gadget for clipping unwelcome suitors' noses is no way to creep into my heart. It may be Volupté to you, but it's only loose thinking to me.

Of the nine designers, only one, Mr. Gilbert Rohde, thinks women's clothes good enough as they are, but he believes men's clothes need radical revision. Mr. Rohde envisions the man of the twenty-first century in a ski suit knitted of a mixture of transparent synthetic yarn and infinitely fine beryllium threads, whose color can be changed by varying the plating of the beryllium copper wire. "The gentleman, for example, may start to the office in a rich gun-metal Solo-suit, drab in color, but scintillating with life. [There's that same dreadful insistence on the material's moiling and churning.] In the afternoon, there is a directors' meeting, so he changes to a deep maroon; and for dinner, the change is made in a jiffy to turquoise." On this man's head Mr. Rohde places an "Antenna Hat," rather similar in design to the coils of a copper still: "It snatches radio and Omega waves out of the ether—here, at last, is man's opportunity to escape from the deadly monotony of the twentieth-century male hat." The delightful prospect of having Guy Lombardo playing about your head and ears is enough to stir the pulse of the most apathetic. Mr. Man of Tomorrow will further wear a modish surtout called the Plastivest, fashioned of Plexiglas—two words, incidentally, which I will thank Mr. Rohde to tow out to sea and burn at his earliest convenience. This appalling little vest is designed to contain a two-way telephone, radio set, office equipment, and control switches for the air waves which heat and cool the suit. The feet, presumably with streamlined bunions, are to be encased in nothing more or less than congress gaiters "with breather pores just large enough for air, but too small for water"; and, finally, men will have returned to wearing long hair and marcelled beards in the fashion of Artaxerxes. "And perhaps we shall find a few platinum blondes, too," murmurs Mr. Rohde engagingly.

For two days now I have been crouching in a corner of this coal bin, enjoying a peace I never thought possible. Of course, the grit gets in your teeth and there's a leak in that pipe overhead, but on the other hand it's just a trifle too dark for reading. Why, you couldn't even see your hand before your face, particularly if it were holding a copy of *Vogue*. And goodness knows, it'll be a long time before it's steady enough for that.

Midwinter Facial Trends

A scenario writer I know, who had been working uninterruptedly in Hollywood for three years, finally got back to New York for a two-week vacation. He had barely unpacked his gold-backed military hairbrushes and put on a red moiré smoking jacket when a wire from his agent ordered him back to the Coast for an assignment. The young man preferred to stay, but his conscience reminded him of the two hundred and fifty thousand dollars in annuities he was carrying, and this in turn summoned up a frightening picture of a destitute old age when he might have to work on a newspaper again and ride in streetcars. After wrestling with himself for several hours, he decided to assert his independence. He sent back a spunky wire to the effect that he was working on a novel and could not return under any conditions unless his salary was raised to seventeen hundred and fifty dollars a week, instead of fifteen hundred. Then he forgot all about it, except to lie awake three nights and stay indoors waiting for the telephone to ring.

To nobody's surprise, the deal went through, and forty-eight hours later the scenario writer was sitting in a producer's office in Hollywood, a little worse for the plane trip and a box of sodium Amytal tablets. In a few badly chosen words the producer explained his predicament. He had a terrific story; it smelled box office a mile away. But every writer on the payroll had been stumped for the last three months by one detail.

"I'll tell you the meat of the story," said the producer. "It's got plenty of spontinuity when you maul it over in your mind, only just this one little thing you got to figure out."

"Give," murmured the scenario writer, closing his eyes to indicate that his faculties were purring like a Diesel engine.

"We fade in on a street in London," began the producer, fading in on a street in London. "It's about four o'clock in the morning and I see a guy dressed in rags dragging himself along through the fog, a Lon Chaney type guy. He's all twisted and crippled up. *Voom*! All of a sudden he ducks down an areaway and knocks on a door. It opens and I see a gorgeous hallway with Chinese rugs and Ming vases. We hold the camera on it and milk whatever we can from the scene. The minute the guy's inside, he straightens up, takes off this harness, and unties his leg. What I mean is, the guy's as normal as you or me. Any audience'll buy that—am I right? Then we truck with him through a door and he's in like a hospital corridor. He pulls on rubber gloves and an operating gown—"

"Wait a minute," the writer interrupted, rising. "Am I supposed to spot laughs in this?"

"Siddown," commanded the producer. "There's a million opportunities for good crazy dialogue later on.

We wipe the guy into an operating room and pan around. He's got ten, fifteen beautiful dames chained to the walls with practically nothing on, and if that don't kill 'em, I don't know show business. The legal department's taking it up with the Hays office this afternoon. We follow the guy over to a bench that's full of test tubes and scientific stuff; he pours one test tube into another and hollers, 'I got it! The life secret I been hunting for years!' Mind you, this ain't dialogue—I'm just spitballing. So then he puts a little of this life secret in a hypodermic needle and rings a gong. These two assistants wheel in a table with our leading woman on it, out like a light. Our guy rubs his hands and laughs like a hyena. He picks up the hypo, bends over our girl, and that's where you got to figure out this one thing."

"What's that?" the writer inquired suspiciously. The producer bit the end off a manufacturer's size Corona, frustration in his eyes, and shook his head.

"What kind of a business is this guy in?" he asked helplessly.

If you are inclined to brood easily, I can guarantee that this question will tease you to the brink of hysteria. It obsessed me almost constantly until I stumbled across what may very well be the answer. It is contained in a little 134-page brochure entitled *Cosmetic Surgery*, by Charles C. Miller, M.D., published by the author in 1907. Since that day several weeks ago when I first peeped into this attractive volume, bound in red sharkskin, I have been confined to my rooms in the Albany with a fairly constant attack of the rams. As if Dr. Miller's prose style were not sufficiently graphic, the text is supplemented with half a dozen photographs

21

and a score of drawings calculated to make your scalp tingle. I am no sissy, but I will risk a sporting flutter of half a guinea that even the brothers Mayo would have flinched under *Cosmetic Surgery*.

The author starts off casually enough with instructions for correcting outstanding ears, which range all the way from tying them flat to the head to some pretty violent surgery. Personally, I have found that a short length of three-quarter-inch Manila hemp bound stoutly about the head, the knot protruding below one's felt hat, adds a rakish twist to the features and effectively prisons ears inclined to flap in the wind. A salty dash may be imparted to the ensemble by dipping the rope in tar, or even substituting oakum for hemp.

I must confess that the chapter headed "Nose with the Bulbous Tip," on page 50, fired my blood, and I read three or four pages avidly waiting for the appearance of Hercule Poirot or even Inspector Lestrade before I discovered that no crime had been committed. But on page 79, just as I finished yawning through some hints on diminishing the unduly large mouth by hemstitching it at the corners, Dr. Miller plucked the roses from my cheeks with "Marginal Tattooing as a Means of Adding to the Apparent Width of the Lips." That may not be your idea of a punchy title for the marquee of a theatre, but if Boris Karloff were in it, you'd pay your six-sixty fast enough. Living as I do on the hem of the wilderness, I was not aware that "tattooing about the margin of the lips to overcome undue thinness" had become a commonplace. The technique is as follows: "The skin is punctured or pricked open with a needle. The puncturing does not extend through the skin, but merely into the true skin [Come, come, Doctor, let's not quibble.] After the punctures have been made, the coloring is rubbed in with the point of the needle or with a slightly flattened spud. Some reaction may be expected to follow the operation, but healing is complete in a few days." Why any reaction save boredom should follow rubbing a patient's lips with a potato is not clear to me, but I suppose that if one were allergic to potatoes, one might become restless under the massage. Speaking for myself, I have always been very partial to potatoes, especially those of the cottage-fried type.

It is on page 92, with "The Formation of the Dimple," that Dr. Miller really removes the buttons from the foils. "It is my practice in these cases," he states, "to thoroughly scrub the cheek, and then, after having the patient smile, select the point where a dimple should form under ordinary circumstances…. I mark this point, and insert my hypodermic needle." The operative method from now on is strikingly similar to fishing for perch through a hole in the ice. The Doctor lowers a line with a bobber and a bit of red flannel, builds a fire on the patient's forehead, and sits down to warm his hands till a dimple is hooked. The patient lies there softly whimpering, "I didn't have enough trouble, I had to have dimples like Robert Taylor yet!" And there let us leave them in the softly flickering firelight, with the thought that it will flicker much better if you pile on an occasional page out of *Cosmetic Surgery*, by Charles C. Miller.

The Body Beautiful

Sometimes when I have worked for hours in vain over a difficult problem in Baker Street and my keen hawklike profile is drawn with fatigue, I like to take down my Stradivarius, pile it on the fire and curl up with a copy of *Hygeia*, the monthly magazine published by the American Medical Association. I don't necessarily have to read it; all I have to do is curl up with it. In a few minutes my pulse becomes normal, my eyes glaze over, and I am ready to do business with the Sandman. I don't know much about medicine but I know what I like. If the American Medical Association would only put up this magazine in tablet or powder form nobody would ever pass a white night again. Unlike other soporifics, *Hygeia* does not affect the heart; I have even read a copy without any ill effects other than a feeling of drowsiness the next day. It fulfills every requirement of the United States Pharmacopeia; it is clean, it is fresh every month, and it is standard strength. From the opening essay on flat feet down to the very last article on diabetic muffins, it is a guaranteed yawn from cover to cover.

The one oasis in this Sahara, however, is a sort of outpatient clinic where the layman is allowed to make a fool of himself in full view of the medical profession. I quote at random (random hell, I had to look through nineteen copies to find it) a letter headed "Synthetic Saliva" appearing in the Q. and A. department of *Hygeia*:

"To the Editor:—How could saliva be duplicated? Where could the proper materials be secured to duplicate it or nearly so?—H.C.D., Illinois."

Here is a cry from the heart. Obviously some young Frankenstein has built himself a monster or Golem in his spare time out in the woodshed. With infinite labor and utmost secrecy, using bits of wire, tin, old bones and meat, he has created the perfect robot. Suddenly, on the verge of completion, he stops in sudden panic. He has left out saliva. The monster is beginning to growl ominously; he wants what all the other boys on the street have. But do you think the editors of *Hygeia* care? They fob off H.C.D. (possibly one of the most brilliant inventors of our time) with a few heavy-duty medical words and sink into a complacent snooze, unmindful that a raging monster with a dry mouth may be loose in the Middle West at this very moment. I don't like to be an alarmist, fellows, but this is a very short-sighted attitude.

No matter how blasé they imagine themselves, hypochondriacs from six to sixty will get a deep and ghoulish satisfaction studying the correspondence which appears each month. Those private maladies you have been pruning and transplanting couldn't possibly compare with the things that bother *Hygeia* readers. The pathetic query of J.I.B., Pennsylvania, will illustrate:

"To the Editor:—Is there any danger of contracting radium poisoning from the use of clocks painted with a radium compound; for instance, in case the clock crystal should be broken and the radium compound chipped off?"

The editors, who pretend to know everything, reply that there is no danger whatsoever. This is pretty cold comfort to a man who probably glows like a Big Ben every time he enters a dark room. However, he might as well stop barking up the wrong tree; he wouldn't get a civil answer from *Hygeia* even if he grew a minute hand and sounded the hour and half-hour with a musical chime.

I would like to think that the case of G.S., Ohio, is also one of hypochondria but it has a more ominous ring:

"To the Editor:—Can the statements contained in a recent daily newspaper that bobbing the hair will cause girls to grow beards be verified? Or is it just a bit of propaganda?"

If that isn't a tacit admission that Miss G.S. is sporting a grogan or an imperial around Ohio, I knock under. Even if she only *thinks* she has a beard, I wouldn't give her house-room; but that is beside the point, as she has not asked me for house-room. She probably has the whole house to herself anyway. Much more understandable is the plight of the frightened Kansan who writes as follows:

"To the Editor:—My students tell me that surgeons have been able to transplant the stomach from an animal, as a calf or a goat, into man. Is this possible?— N.B.Z., Kansas."

I can sympathize with the poor fellow for I, too, get the same sensation when I drink black velvet. Actually, it only *feels* as if you had changed stomachs with a goat.

One morning I even woke up convinced that I had swallowed a marble the night before. To make it worse, a man named Mr. Coffee-Nerves was standing over my bed in a white Prince Albert, helping me to hate myself. I got up and went right through him to the bathroom where I had a long look at my chest. At first I couldn't tell whether it was a steelie or a bull's-eye, but it turned out to be a clear glass agate with a little lamb inside. I managed to dissolve my marble with two aspirins in a glass of hot water. But thank God *I'm* no hypochondriac; you don't catch *me* writing letters to the American Medical Association.

For a refreshing contrast to *Hygeia*, one turns to a live-wire little monthly called *Estes Back to Nature Magazine*, published at 113 North LaBrea Avenue, Hollywood, California. Its editor is Dr. St. Louis Estes, who modestly styles himself "Discoverer of Brain Breathing and Dynamic Breath Controls for Disease Prevention and Life Extension, Father and Founder of the Raw Food Movement, and International Authority on Old Age and Raw Foods." (*There* is something to write on a library card when they ask you for your occupation.) Cooked vegetables, spices, and hair tonic are poison, says Dr. Estes, and although I have never tried the combination, I can readily believe it. But the Doctor is constructive, and I know no better answer to the cynicism and bigotry of *Hygeia* than a menu I found in his magazine. It was labelled "A Dinner Fit for a King" and it still haunts me:

"EGG AND FRUIT SOUP: To one quart of milk and one pint of cream, beat in thoroughly four eggs. Use as a filler cubed pineapple, sweeten to taste with honey. Serve in cups like broth.

"MOCK TURKEY—WHITE MEAT: Into one pound of cottage cheese mix and roll equal amount of raw flaked pecans, peanuts and jordan almonds, until it becomes a thick, solid mass. Season to taste with chopped onions, pimientos, green peppers, adding a dash of powdered celery, sage and horseradish. Serve in slices like white meat.

"MAPLE ICE CREAM: To one pint of whipped cream add one pint of pure maple syrup. Whip until thick. Then add the beaten whites of two eggs and one cupful of chopped nuts. Freeze."

I froze.

What am I Doing Away From Home?

When I was growing up in New Guinea, or coming of age in Samoa, or whatever the hell I was doing about the age of thirteen, I had occasion to spend a considerable part of my life in hotels. To this day the subtle bouquet of brass polish, hotel carpeting, and rubber plants does more to recall my youth than a dozen faded albums. Mind you, this is no bid for sympathy. I did all right, even if I was the youngest patient in the history of the Keeley Cure. At least I could hold up my end in a group of travelling men discussing the Raines Law, which is more than can be said for certain milksops at Groton and St. George's.

What little scar tissue I carry from those early experiences, however, leaps into bas-relief at a publication of the Pennsylvania Hotels Association called *Live*. Its high purpose, according to a foreword, is "to tell you a few things about hotels you may not know...to show you how well a hotel cares for its guests no matter when they arrive or how tired or hungry they are." Judging from one anecdote, it sets about it in a fairly oblique manner:

Many years ago a foreigner, the guest of a hotel, wanted

29

something done to his dress coat. He summoned a maid, but, unable to speak English, could do nothing but indicate his wishes by drawing his hand across the waist of the coat. It seemed obvious that he wanted the coattails cut off and she was about to send for the valet. He protested, urging her to do the job. She procured a scissors, cut off the tails and sewed the raw edges as best she could. When he returned, he was furious. Much later it turned out he only wanted the coattails pinned back—a job he could easily have done himself. To his credit, he goodnaturedly agreed the joke was on him.

There is an air of dreadful, inhuman gaiety about the tale that freezes the marrow in one's bones. What grim rigadoon was this foreigner about to attend that he must have his coat-tails pinned back, what concourse of ghouls? I can almost see the ghastly grin lighting up his sunken face—if you can call it a face—as he agreed that the joke was on him. I'll thank the Pennsylvania Hotels Association to omit these fiendish vignettes if they want my custom.

And they certainly do—passionately, unreservedly, for on Page 8 of their brochure they offer twenty-seven prizes for the best essay on "Why I Like to Stop at a Hotel." "If you have ever stopped at a hotel—even for one night—you are eligible for this contest," they urge. Well, kids, I stopped at a hotel one night a while back, and in Pennsylvania, too. Not only am I eligible, but now that I've got the floor, you just try to take it away from me. I don't want a prize; all I want is a hearing.

Some years ago a small gasket which controls the plumbing in my country home gave way without warning, and while the plumbers were awaiting a duplicate from Cartier's, I tied a foxtail to the radiator of my Jordan cabriolet and went touring. Night found me at a crossroads before a spacious establishment with a handsome mansard roof and the inviting legend "Snapper Suppers." With many a cry of "Oh, dem snapper suppers!" and "Oh, dat succulent spoon bread wid cloudy honey fresh out ob de hive!" I flung myself on the dollar-and-a-quarter table d'hôte. The snapper supper turned out to have been prefabricated in Camden, New Jersey, and, dulling my hunger with something called a "spamwich" and a cup of lava, I mounted to my room. It was dominated by the bed, a sizable Victorian affair with a mattress easily two inches thick. Anticipating that guests might want to read in bed, the management had thoughtfully strung a naked electric bulb twelve feet away from the ceiling. I read the *Hotel Men's Guide* until my eyes rolled around the counterpane like marbles, and then turned in. The light was scarcely off before the wicker furniture began a slow, sinister gavotte around the room, creaking and groaning like Foxe's *Book of Martyrs*. Simultaneously automobile headlights started flashing across the bay window opposite my bed, and I realized that Dead Man's Carrefour was in for a night of brisk traffic. I was lying there trying to distinguish the lady motorists by the way the brakes screeched on the curve, when the voices went into action in the bar below.

At first they were pitched in a low, rasping hum devoid of vowels, somewhat like Icelandic but more bestial. As time wore on they became interwoven with sharp cries and commands of "Glonfy!" and "Rehume!" None of the words was quite audible, and as a result I had to keep every faculty tense. For a while I courted the theory that a group of Mr. Joyce's admirers were reading aloud from

Finnegans Wake, but suddenly somebody started to break the spindles out of the back of a Windsor chair, using an old-fashioned brass spittoon. I pounded on the floor; he cheerily beat an answering tattoo on the ceiling. I now decided to put my faith in the barbiturates, let the chips fall where they might, and swallowing several capsules that would have killed me had I been a horse, I crept back into my burrow.

A delightful surprise awaited me. Some sort of foreign body inside the pillow now insisted on obtruding into the back of my neck, a space ordinarily reserved for the caresses of wealthy middle-aged women. The obstruction seemed to be cylindrical, yielding to the touch, and about two and a half inches long—in short, the exact size and consistency of a roll of bills. The more I thought about it, the more convinced I became that I had unwittingly stumbled across a cache. And if size meant anything, the world was mine. I exultantly began planning how I would track down Baron Danglars, what I would do to Mercedes the fair Catalan. All that remained was to open the pillow. Any fool can open a pillow, I cackled.

It took me twenty minutes to realize that here was one fool who couldn't, armed with nothing more than a toothbrush, a comb and a commode. I hacked and tore at the seams of that pillow until my fingertips bled and I sobbed aloud with vexation. Meanwhile, in the bar below, the *Walpurgisnacht* was in full swing. On the stairs outside my room they were re-enacting Israel Putnam's escape from the British, and every so often somebody in the room overhead broke into a waltz clog in a pair of specially built lead shoes. Whether it was frustration, Sedormid, or both which finally got me, I'll never know. But this I do know: from now on I'm strictly the Scholar Gipsy, with a knapsack and a bit of bread and cheese snapping at my heels. It may be hot in a haystack, but by God, it's private.

Tomorrow—Fairly Cloudy

Heaven knows I don't want to sound gossipy, but something rather important has been happening to American advertising. In fact, it almost looks as if there might be no American advertising one of these days.

Perhaps a few of you in the Older Business Boys' Division will recall an advertisement which appeared in the late twenties. It showed a well-known Russian princess clasping a Knopf book and bore the starry-eyed admission, "Mindful of my duty to the public, I am careful never to be seen without a Borzoi book." At that time I thought I heard the muffled tread of the *Jacquerie* in the streets and I even went so far as to buy myself a pike suitable for carrying heads. I guess it was merely a case of wishful thinking. Great, fatuous booby that I was, I imagined advertising would be destroyed from the outside. It won't; it's going to bubble and heave and finally expire in the arms of two nuns, like Oscar Wilde.

The opening note of the *marche funèbre* was sounded in an advertisement for Listerine tooth paste in a recent issue of the *American Home*. It was a cartoon strip called "What Put Patty in the Movies?" and its plot was as follows: Patty, a zestful little breastful, crouches on a beach, daydreaming with her two chums. From her

34

mouth issues a balloon with the caption, "I read somewhere there's a great call for photographers' models. Wouldn't I like to be one...lots of money and a chance at the movies maybe." "Why not, Patty?" urges Bob. "You'd be sure to succeed. I'll get Dad to call up his photographer friend, Mr. Hess."

In less than two panels, Mr. Hess is breaking the bad news to Patty. "I'm afraid you won't do, Miss Patty. Your teeth are good, but *not good enough*. For camera work they have to be perfect." To Miss Jones, Mr. Hess' secretary, Patty sobs out her chagrin. "I've failed, Miss Jones... and we needed the money so badly!" "Failed! Fiddlesticks!" counters Miss Jones briskly. "All you need to do is use a special type of tooth paste that our best models and screen stars use. LISTERINE TOOTH PASTE is its name. Try it two weeks...then come back."

Well, sir, you're probably psychic. "Three Weeks Later—at the Studio" introduces the fifth picture, in which Mr. Hess announces, "The job's yours, Miss Patty...$50 a week. I can't believe you're the same girl. Your teeth are simply perfect." "I'm so thankful, Mr. Hess," replies Patty, who is a bulldog for tenacity. "It may lead to the movies. And all the credit is due to Miss Jones." The sixth and last panel is headed "One Year Later." On the observation platform of a train, surrounded by the upturned faces of townsfolk, stands Patty, her smart tailleur festooned with orchids. "You're all so wonderful. Good-bye! Good-bye!" she calls. "She'll click in Hollywood," observes Bob stoutly to Patty's girl chum, and it is Patty's nameless girl chum whose answer should go echoing down the corridors of time. "Maybe we'd better start using LISTERINE TOOTH PASTE too," she murmurs drearily. *"Anything to get out of this hick town."*

The italics are mine, but the desperation is that of the whole advertising confraternity. So all the old tactics have finally broken down—wheedling, abuse, snobbery and terror. I look forward to the last great era in advertising, a period packed with gloom, defeatism and frustration, in which spectacles like the following will be a commonplace:

(Scene: The combination cellar and playroom of the Bradley home in Pelham Manor. Mr. and Mrs. Bradley and their two children, Bobby and Susie, are grouped about their new automatic oil burner. They are all in faultless evening dress, including Rover, the family Airedale.)

Bobby—Oh, Moms, I'm so glad you and Dads decided to install a Genfeedco automatic oil burner and air conditioner with the new self-ventilating screen flaps plus finger control! It is noiseless, cuts down heating bills, and makes the air we breathe richer in vita-ray particles!

Susie—Think of it! Actual experiments performed by trained engineers under filtered water prove that certain injurious poisons formerly found in cellars are actually cut down to thirty-four per cent by switching to a Genfeedco!

Mr. Bradley (*tonelessly*)—Well, I suppose anything's better than a heap of slag at this end of the cellar.

Mrs. Bradley—Yes, and thanks to Buckleboard, the new triple-ply, satin-smooth, dirt-resisting wall plastic, we now have an ugly little playroom where we can sit and loathe each other in the evening.

Bobby—Hooray for Buckleboard! Since Dads made

this feedbin into a playroom, no more hanging around the livery stable with questionable acquaintances!

MR. BRADLEY—Yes, we now have a livery stable right in our own home. The initial expense was brutal, but the money only gathered two and a half per centum in the bank.

BOBBY and SUSIE (*munching candy bars*)—Hooray! Hooray for this new taste sensation!

MRS. BRADLEY—Harvey, I'm worried about the children. Don't you think they have too much energy?

SUSIE—Choc-Nugs are just *loaded* with energy, Moms! These crackly nuggets of purest Peruvian cocoa, speckled with full-flavored, rain-washed nut meats, call forth a chorus of "Yums" from every wide-awake girl and boy!

BOBBY—In Mexico it's "Viva el Choc-Nugo!" but in America its "Hooray for Choc-Nugs!" Any way you pronounce it, it is pronounced "Goodylicious" by millions of eager candy-lovers!

MR. BRADLEY—I see that I have fathered a couple of Yahoos....Bobby, answer the door.

BOBBY—Had we installed a set of Zings, the new electric chime, it would not be necessary for callers to wait outside in the rain and sleet...

MR. BRADLEY—Answer the door or I will knock your block off, you murdering little saw-toothed ape. (*Bobby goes to door, admits Mr. and Mrs. Fletcher and their three children, attired in long balbriggan underwear. General greetings.*)

MRS. FLETCHER—Don't mind us, Verna, we just dropped in to sneer at your towels. (*Unfolding a towel*) My, they're so absorbent and fluffy, aren't they? You know, they're made of selected fibres culled from high-grade flat-tailed Montana sheep subject to rigid inspection by qualified sheep inspectors.

Mrs. Bradley (*listlessly*)—They fall apart in two days, but we got tired of using blotters.

Mrs. Fletcher—Verna, I think it's about time you and I had a heart-to-heart talk about your skin. You're as rough and scaly as an old piece of birch-bark.

Mrs. Bradley—I know; it's my own fault. I neglected my usual beauty cocktail.

Mrs. Fletcher—Skins, you know, are divided into three types—cameo, butter-scotch, and mock nutria. Yours defies classification.

Mrs. Bradley (*miserably*)—Oh, how can I win back my Prince Charming?

Mrs. Fletcher—Why not follow the example of glamorous Mrs. Barney Kessler, socially prominent matron of the Main Line?

Mrs. Bradley—What does she do?

Mrs. Fletcher—Each morning, on rising, she scrubs her skin with an ordinary sink-brush. Then she gently pats in any good brand of vanishing cream until Kessler disappears to his office.

Mrs. Bradley—And then?

Mrs. Fletcher—I can't remember, but she's got a complexion like a young girl.

Mr. Fletcher—Say, Harvey, make this test for yourself. Do some brands of pipe tobacco irritate your tongue, cause your eyeballs to capsize in your head? Then pack your old briar with velvety Pocahontas Mixture and know true smoke-ease. After all, you have to put something into your pipe. You can't just sit there like a bump on a log.

MR. BRADLEY—I get along all right smoking old leaves from my lawn.

MR. FLETCHER—Yes, but look at the fancy tin these people give you. Remember that five hundred of these tins and a fifty-word essay on "Early Kentish Brass Rubbings" entitle you to the Pocahontas Mixture vacation offer, whereby you retire at sixty with most of your faculties impaired.

MRS. FLETCHER—Er—Fred, don't you think it's time we....

MR. FLETCHER—Now, Harriet, don't interrupt. Can't you see I'm talking to Harvey Bradley?

MRS. FLETCHER (*timidly*)—I know, but there seems to be about two feet of water in this cellar and it's rising steadily.

MR. BRADLEY (*sheepishly*)—I guess I should have specified Sumwenco Super-Annealed Brass Pipe throughout. My contractor warned me at the time.

MR. FLETCHER (*bailing like mad with his tin*)—Well, this is a pretty how-do-you-do.

MRS. BRADLEY (*comfortably*)—At least, whatever else happens, under the Central American Mutual Perpetual Amortizational Group Insurance Plan our loved ones need not be reduced to penury.

MRS. FLETCHER—What good is that? Our loved ones are right here with us!

MR. BRADLEY (*mildly*)—You don't tell me.

MRS. BRADLEY—I always say the added protection is worth the difference, don't you, Harvey? (*She pats her husband's shoulder reassuringly as they all drown like rats in a trap.*)

Whereas, the Former Premises Being Kaput—

I was backed into a corner at a party last week with a couple named either Swineforth or Twyeffort—between the melee and their tutti-frutti delivery, I never found out which—and was nearing the point where you scream to equalize the pressure when my wife hewed her way through the crush and, much to my surprise, greeted the pair as though they really existed.

"You remember them, don't you?" she shouted into my ear trumpet as they flapped away to eviscerate someone else. "They lived in the studio across from us in the Aragon. He was the treasurer of the tenants' committee." I naturally gave her the benefit of the doubt and assumed she was talking gibberish, but after a while their faces took on a horrid familiarity, and the whole episode, encrusted with lichen, came back to me. It fair gives you a turn, the way you can expunge the past. I daresay I pass the place—the new building, that is—almost every time I get down to the Village, yet I can't seem to associate myself with that corner. I only remember the one the Swineforths (or Twyefforts) backed me into.

The Aragon, as we knew it, was a five-story affair of

mellowed brick with a cool marble foyer and a walled garden containing a fountain, as gracious a dwelling as ever adorned the Washington Square area. Contrary to the widespread belief that it was a historic old family mansion, it dated back only to 1927, when the three brownstones composing it were remodelled and given a common façade. Its residents were also rather routine—statisticians and wool factors, a heavy concentration of affluent elderly widows, and the usual complement of walking dead that one meets in any New York apartment elevator. The most glamorous tenant, but so rarely visible during waking hours that few knew he lived there, was Archie Carmine, the celebrated Broadway producer. Archie, a legend in his own lifetime, is a pale, unshaven wraith of a man whose patent-leather eyes have the glitter of a fer-de-lance's and whose reputation is no less lethal. Though admittedly a genius, he devours whomever he loves at the moment, and it is a canon around Sardi's that any traffic with him is a passport to a nervous breakdown. Novels have been written about Archie's perfidy; playwrights and actors quit rooms at the mere rumor of his approach, scenic designers turn lilac at his name. My own relationship with him was ideal, never having been sullied by business, and I always enjoyed his tirades against the critics and the decline of the theater when he glided into the lobby of the Aragon, his fangs still dripping from some midnight conference.

For about a year, there was disquieting talk that our building was up for sale, that it was going to be converted into a wax-works, that New York University had leased it to accommodate courses in square dancing, that Trans-Jordan was eying the site for a legation, et cetera. Something obviously was cooking, because every other month the name of a different landlord would appear on the rent bill—strange corporations like the Sword of Damocles Holding Company and Samjo Realty Associates. It was manifest that the property was being traded daily at Longchamps by dapper, aromatic men in sharkskin and effulgent neckties, and life suddenly became precarious. One morning, the suspense ended. We were notified that the Moloch Management Company had acquired the premises and that we were to vacate on the double, as demolition was to begin shortly. The same day, the newspapers carried an interview with Alex Moloch, head of the organization, describing the skyscraper he intended to erect on the plot and the four or five adjoining it. To conform to the rich artistic tradition of the neighborhood, he declared, the ground floor would contain exhibition halls where local painters could show their work. A jar of free tuning forks would be available at all times in the lobby for composers, and any sculptor leasing one of the top-floor studios—the rents of which were to start at five hundred dollars a month—would receive a spatula and fifty pounds of clay. Without actually bracketing himself with Lorenzo de' Medici, Moloch grew quite lyrical as he visualized the role he and the edifice would play in New York's cultural life.

That evening, a dozen of us at the Aragon, who had never exchanged more than nods and grunts, assembled and pledged ourselves to resist. Archie Carmine sent word by the doorman that unavoidable business had summoned him to the Coast but that he was in the fray

to the finish. The meeting was, for the most part, consumed in parliamentary wrangling; most of those
present, apparently, had never had any audience beyond
their husbands or wives, and, once on their feet, strayed
off into irrelevancies as windy as a Senate filibuster. At
length, however, a measure of cohesion obtained, and we
appointed a chairman, a vibrant, knifelike accountant
with a Rand School manner, named Fessenden. Swineforth (or Twyeffort) was elected treasurer, not for his
financial acumen but because his wife's mink coat
inspired confidence. Then a per-capita levy to hire an
attorney was imposed, and a publicity junto chosen to
awaken sympathy for our plight, and we adjourned in an
orgy of self-congratulation. The Moloch Management
crowd was practically on the run, we jubilantly assured
each other. It just proved that a few spunky people could
trounce a big, soulless corporation if they stuck together.

Unfortunately, the opposition refused to be awed.
Deriding our tocsin in the press to the effect that the
city's most historic landmark was about to be razed, our
new landlord called us a bunch of plutocrats hypo-
critically bent on preserving cheap rents. He drew an
affecting portrait of himself as an altruist whose sole
aim was to provide adequate housing. "Ever since I was
a poor East Side boy, I have carried a dream in my
heart," he went on, and disclosed how, as an urchin, he
used to haunt Washington Square and envision the
mammoth structure, designed to shelter the common
man, that he would build on our corner. This arrant
humbug evoked a counterblast from us, of course, and
for weeks thereafter the newspapers boiled with
recriminations and pontifical statements by architects,

civic planners, and all kinds of busybodies. Meanwhile, in the background, the legal battle was under way. Our respective lawyers bombarded each other with writs and stays, hearings were constantly being scheduled, and almost daily some fresh ukase full of judicial argle-bargle found its way under our doors.

At three o'clock one winter morning, I was wrenched out of bed by a series of peremptory rings on our doorbell. Arming myself with a Balinese kris, I cautiously slid back the bolt. The scourge of Broadway, Archie Carmine, confronted me, wrapped in a polo coat and swaying like a Lombardy poplar. His face was cadaverous, even for him, and when he spoke he exuded a wave of cognac that nearly felled me.

"Crisake, are you in bed *already?*" he demanded with indignation. "What are you, a farmer or something?" I started to protest the intrusion, but he cut me short. "Look, cousin, better not waste any time sleeping," he said darkly. "A hell of a situation's come up here. You know what I heard when I got home just now? Some bastard's planning to tear this building down!"

As gently as I could, I reminded him that everyone, including myself, had known about it for months. "And while we're on it," I added, keeping my shoulder braced against the door, "I wish you'd pony up your end of the legal fee to Swineforth and get him off my neck. Every time I see him, he asks me where you are, why you're avoiding him—"

"Oh, he thinks I'm not good for it, does he?" Archie roared. "Why, I'll break his bloody arm! Where is he, the little mope? Which apartment is he in? What does he look like?"

It took the guile of Machiavelli (who happened to be sleeping in our foyer) to calm Archie down and persuade him to retire, but before he left he vowed to appear at the next tenants' meeting with an abysmally simple program for saving the house. He had it all worked out, every last detail, and he would outline it so that even chowderheads like us could comprehend it. As I had anticipated, he failed to turn up, either then or at subsequent meetings, and, whatever his reasons, he showed rare judgment. Each gathering was, if possible, more tedious than the last. Fessenden, our chairman, began fancying himself another Gladstone, and delivered long, rambling speeches that made one's teeth ache with boredom. The schemes to publicize our cause grew steadily loonier: a tag day, a parade, proposals to bomb Moloch's offices or chain ourselves like suffragettes to the hydrant outside the Aragon. As the months wore on, an air of doom invaded the building. One by one, doormen and elevator operators disappeared, until only a frowzy alcoholic was left to tend the furnace, distribute the mail, and police the lobby. A number of the tenants, deciding that the conclusion was foregone, moved out, and finally, inescapably, the court handed down the fiat that sealed our destiny. The thirty-day eviction notice did not shilly-shally. Anyone found on the premises one hour later would be taken by the scruff of his neck and dropped, together with his chattels, into the Washington Square fountain. It was all over but the snuffling and the thud of the wreckers' crowbars.

Of the thirteen souls who assembled in Fessenden's apartment for the wake, at least six were old ladies in jet chokers and bombazine. The rest were idealists like me, lured by a rumor that the money in the kitty was to be apportioned among us. It proved baseless; in fact, as Swineforth's report incontrovertibly showed, we each owed twenty-two dollars for stamps and mimeographing. Fessenden had just embarked on a punishing valedictory when the doorbell pealed. My wife tiptoed out, and reappeared in a moment with a nonplused expression. Behind her stalked Archie Carmine, clad in pajamas and a rumpled blue moiré dressing gown and bearing a highball. Someone must have recognized him, for an excited buzz spread through the room. For such a mythical figure to appear, and, moreover, *en déshabillé*, was a sensation, and Archie, always the show-man, exploited it to the utmost. Magnanimously signaling to Fessenden to proceed, he thrust his glass into a pocket, sat down, and fell into an attitude of deep meditation, like Rodin's "Thinker."

"Gassed," my wife confided tersely in my ear. "Absolutely loaded. He'll erupt in about ten minutes."

Her prediction was conservative; Fessenden had barely managed to restore ennui before Archie raised his hand.

"Pardon me, friend," he said with what he supposed was courtly elegance. "Give us the floor a second, will you?" He rose unsteadily and took up a position at stage center, in front of the fireplace. "Folks, I've been following this discussion closely, and if I may say so, it's a lot of pazooza. You're tackling the problem all wrong. You want to save the building, do you? Well, I'll tell you how to do it." He lowered his voice dramatically. "Call up Bernie Baruch."

"Baruch?" Swineforth repeated, openmouthed.

"But it's too late! We've been ordered to move. They've torn the ivy off the walls—"

"It's never too late, Buster," Archie interrupted. "The only thing that'll work now is drag. You need a really important figure to go to bat for you, and he's the gee who can do it. Yes, sir, I'll make book on him. If anybody in the world can save the Aragon, he can."

"Sure, but how do we approach him?" Fessenden demurred. "After all, he's our elder statesman, one of the most distinguished men in the country."

"Duck soup," said Archie airily. "I just call up Billy Rose, he gives Bernie a bell, and we're in like a burglar."

There was an electric pause; then a confused babble filled the room. "Did you hear that?" the old ladies queried each other feverishly. "Bernard Baruch is going to help us!...Yes, yes, it's all decided....That man is a close friend of his....No, dear, not an invalid, he's a big theatrical producer....He's with Klaw & Erlanger—you know, the Shubert people....My numerologist *told* me there'd be a dark stranger with a miracle....I don't understand—do we pay our rent to Mr. Baruch now?"

Fessenden, his eyes dilated with excitement, beat on a table for silence. "Wait a minute, *please*!" he besought everyone. "Let's observe the rules of order! Mr. Carmine has generously offered to intercede in our behalf. Do I hear any objections?"

"Objections!" someone exclaimed. "Why, we ought to present him with a medal. It's a marvelous idea, an inspiration!"

One of the ladies, a portly beldam with a blue marcel and harlequin glasses, waved importunately. "May I ask the chair a question?" she called out. "I think the basic idea is splendid, but, Mr. Carmine, are you sure that Bernard Baruch is the right person for us to appeal to?"

"*Who?*" Archie inquired, staring at her as though his ears had deceived him. She repeated the name, and simultaneously the avalanche, so long overdue, descended. Like a small British car turning in its own wheelbase, Archie executed a characteristic switch. "Baruch?" he snarled. "Are you bughouse? What makes you think a man of Baruch's caliber would bother with a lot of pipsqueaks like you? Brother, I've heard some dillies in my day, but that's the payoff. Baruch! Ho-ho—what a yock this'll give the mob at Sardi's!"

In the ensuing hush, no louder than that which pervades any Egyptian tomb, my wife and I dropped on all fours and crept out. Whether Archie escaped intact, we never learned, though instinct tells me he must have. The last we knew, he was living on a seventy-foot ketch off Coral Gables with an auxiliary engine and a Cuban strip teaser. The owner, I understand—or maybe it was her husband—was suing him for eleven months' rent. I'll give him a tip: he hasn't a Chinaman's chance of collecting. As I told our own landlord last month, you can't get blood out of a stone.

My Heart's in the Highlands, and My Neckband, Too

Maybe I'm hypersensitive, but has anybody else noticed how deucedly artless and aboveboard the copy in those Hathaway shirt advertisements is becoming? I mean the ones where the man in the eye patch is engaged in fingering an oboe or hybridizing orchids or riffling through the poems of Gerard Manley Hopkins—pastimes indicative of a patrician taste and, it is tacit, the sort of thing you might develop a flair for if you were similarly attired. The accompanying letterpress, couched in a breezy yet decorous vein, has always avoided shrillness or ballyhoo; it recognizes you quite accurately for what you are, a connoisseur of the finer things—or at least an embryonic one—and merely offers a setting worthy of the jewel. Recently, however, an almost neurotic punctilio has invaded the text. The Hathaway people seem so intent on demonstrating their candor, their utter lack of guile, that they have begun calling attention to nonexistent defects in their product. The last ad I caught showed their Polyphemus against the background of some native Indian state that looked like Jaipur, to judge by the pink architecture and the colorful procession of elephants behind him. He was

49

dressed in pukka garb—sola topee and a swagger blouse—and the caption said, in part,

> This shirt is made of India Madras, which Hathaway imports from India. [As distinguished, one assumes, from India Madras imported from Cedar Rapids.] This is the real stuff, woven by Indian cottagers on their handlooms....The natural dyestuffs used by these Indian cottagers aren't completely color-fast—they fade a little, with washing and sunshine. This gives the shirts a look of good breeding and maturity which no mass-produced fabric can ever aspire to.

The old verbal alchemy, in short, is at work. By an adroit shift of logic, Hathaway has in one breath affirmed its probity and established the canon that it's smart to be weatherbeaten. Confidentially, I plan to bleach everything I own in lye—India lye, of course—including my underthings. Nobody's going to call *me* a parvenu.

For pure winsomeness, though, the apogee in consumer courtship was the advertisement a year or so ago that genuflected to one of the folks who supply Hathaway with its raw material. Under a photograph of an alert cock sparrow of a man surrounded by heaps of cloth was the legend "Hathaway salutes a great Scotsman" and the following panegyric:

> James White of Auchterarder is one of the most unforgettable characters we have ever met. Proud, kindly, adventurous, warmhearted—and perhaps a little dour by American standards. We got to know him in the ordinary way of business—he makes fabrics for Hathaway shirts. But our admiration for Jimmy White goes far beyond our mercantile relations. He is a GREAT MAN. To begin

with, he is one of the shrewdest fishermen on earth, equally wise in the ways of trout and salmon. He is also one of the most brilliant designers of shirtings alive today. His craftsmanship is a magnificent anachronism. For many years he refused to sell his cloth to America. He finally gave in when we trudged five miles to his mill in a heavy rainstorm; he liked that.

That Mr. White is a paragon among weavers, an alloy of the Chevalier Bayard, Balthasar Gobelin, and Izaak Walton, I do not doubt, though what earthly relevance his knack for circumventing fish has to his fabrics is obscure. The thing that cries out for clarification (well, maybe that's too strong; "whimpers" would be closer) is the nature of the tactics Hathaway used to cajole him. Who conceived the idea of the pilgrimage in the rain and made it, and why did it melt the intractable Caledonian? I can't answer these questions, but it so happens that I have here a small proscenium arch, a clump of heather, a safari animated by similar motives—and, what is more, an irresistible urge to weave a playlet. Start the looms, laddie.

SCENE, *a typical Highland glen not a hundred miles from Auchtertochty—in fact, two and a half miles from Auchtertochty. It has been raining steadily for months prior to the rise of the curtain, so that a fearful smog shrouds the glen, but in the weak light filtering through the boscage there is visible an ancient stone footbridge and, huddled beneath it, a quartet clad in rough shooting clothes—Norfolk jackets, gaiters, and waterproofs. They are Finucane, Disbrow, and Ermatinger, executives of an American shirt corporation, and*

Kluckhorn, an advertising man. The morale of the group is at a very low ebb. Kluckhorn, employing a jet lighter, is trying to ignite a pile of wet leaves and brush, and the resulting smoke has thrown his companions into paroxysms of coughing. After a moment, Disbrow, with a stifled oath, rises and kicks apart the smudge.

KLUCKHORN (*aggrievedly*): Hey, that's a hell of a thing to do! It was just starting to catch on!

DISBROW: Aw, go jump in the loch. You may be the fair-haired boy of American advertising, but you're a square when it comes to woodcraft.

KLUCKHORN: Is that so? Why, you big tub of lard, I forgot more—

FINUCANE (*stepping between them*): Oh, dry up, both of you. We've got enough headaches without you two bickering.

ERMATINGER: Damn right. If you ask me, we were fools to ever leave the hotel. Why couldn't that Scotch genius of yours have come over there to see us?

KLUCKHORN: Because he's dour, that's why. Because he don't want any part of you or your shirts.

DISBROW: So we walk five miles in a cloudburst to beg a few crummy bolts of material from a man that hates our guts. That's logical.

KLUCKHORN: He doesn't hate your guts. He doesn't even know you're alive.

FINUCANE: Says you. Didn't I cable him we were planing over from London just to huddle with him?

KLUCKHORN (*patiently*): Look, fellows, I'm not underestimating your importance, but it's time you realized who we're dealing with. Jock Smeed of

Auchtertochty isn't any fly-by-night weaver. He's a world figure, like Chou En-lai or— or Musa Dagh.

ERMATINGER: Yeah, yeah, we heard all that before— he's an authority on salmon. Well, so am I, Nova Scotia and every other kind, but if customers want to see me, they don't have to scramble on their belly through a marsh.

DISBROW: Check. We might as well face it—we're on a wild-goose chase. Even if we find this joker, there's no guarantee he'll cough up the goods. Let's get back to the goddam hotel.

KLUCKHORN: Now, hold on one second. Men, I've got a surprise for you. I didn't want to spill it, but you forced my hand. (*Impressively*) At this exact moment, the four of us are practically within spitting distance of Jock Smeed!

OMNES: What?...Where is he?...What the hell are we waiting for?

KLUCKHORN: Easy, easy-just listen to me. Remember that pub we stopped at—the Moral Quagmire? Well, I had a brain wave and I slipped the barmaid a couple of farthings. She told me that our man takes every Tuesday off to fish, right here in this very glade.

ERMATINGER (*cunningly*): Meaning that we could bump into him accidentally on purpose, give him the old banana oil, and convince him to allot us some cloth?

KLUCKHORN: Bull's-eye. But we've got to play it smart, mind you. We mustn't excite his suspicion. Woo him, tickle his vanity.

FINUCANE: Not such a bum idea. The only knock is—when will he show? I'm starving.

KLUCKHORN: I thought of that, too. Hand me my

knapsack there. (*He burrows into it, extracts a haggis.*)

ERMATINGER: What's *that*, for God's sake?

KLUCKHORN: A sheep's stomach. It's got the liver and lights chopped up inside, mixed with suet and oatmeal.

DISBROW (*with a shudder*): I'd rather die.

KLUCKHORN: Go on, try a piece. Didn't you ever read *Rob Roy*?

DISBROW: Yep, and I read *Dracula*, too, but I still prefer water.

FINUCANE (*suddenly*): Sh-h-h! Someone's coming… Up there, by that rock…

ERMATINGER: It's a woman—no, a man and a woman. Holy cow, they're handcuffed together!

KLUCKHORN: Jeez, maybe we're in the wrong glen. (*A young couple, numb with exhaustion, totter in. The woman is a ravishing ash blonde with a classic profile, her companion a Canadian rancher whose features are not unfamiliar to Scotland Yard. Both are considerably the worse for wear.*)

WOMAN (*breathlessly*): Is this the road to Inveraray?

KLUCKHORN: I couldn't say. We're strangers here ourselves.

MAN: Oh, bother. I say, forgive me, but by any chance have you gentlemen ever heard of an organization called the Thirty-nine Steps?

KLUCKHORN: Not that I recall. Is it a lodge of some sort?

MAN: That's putting it mildly. Anyhow, if you run into a man the tip of whose little finger is missing, tell him I'm looking for him, won't you? Thanks awfully. (*He whisks his fellow captive out.*)

FINUCANE (*suspiciously*): I've seen that pair before.

DISBROW: So have I. I can't think where.

KLUCKHORN: Ah, probably tourists from the Edinburgh Festival—the moors are lousy with 'em. Listen, boys—just so we don't queer the pitch with Smeed, I better be spokesman for the party. You see, whenever Sir Harry Lauder used to come to Buffalo, my grandfather and I—

ERMATINGER: Pss-st, dummy up! There's a guy wading down the brook—

KLUCKHORN (*jubilantly*): That's him, all right—it couldn't be anybody else! Now, remember—cagey. (*A leathery little Scotsman, attired in hip boots and with a creel slung from his back, enters flicking a trout rod. All toothy good will, Kluckhorn advances humming "A Wee Deoch an Doris."*) Good afternoon to you, sir. How are they biting?

MAN: With their mouths.

KLUCKHORN (*convulsed*): Hot ziggety, that's a good one! I must jot it down.

MAN: Do. There's just room enough on your forehead.

KLUCKHORN: I beg pardon?…Oh, yes—yes, of course. Are you from Auchtertochty, by any chance?

MAN: Aye.

KLUCKHORN (*slyly*): Would you be engaged in the textile industry there, I wonder?

MAN: Aye.

KLUCKHORN: But you're equally wise in the ways of trout and salmon, aren't you? (*The other shrugs modestly.*) Well, I'll be jiggered! You must be that brilliant designer of shirtings, Jock Smeed!

MAN: Aye.

KLUCKHORN (*twinkling*): And you're pretty dour, I can see that.

SMEED: You can, eh? Then perhaps you can see into this creel I have here.

KLUCKHORN: Why, no. What *is* in it?

SMEED: Orders. Big, whopping orders from Cluett Peabody, the Manhattan Shirt Company, and Wilson Brothers. (*Producing a thick sheaf of paper*) You should have seen the ones that got away.

DISBROW (*derisively, to Kluckhorn*): Well, spokesman, what's the matter? The cat got your tongue?

KLUCKHORN: I—I was just figuring out my next move.

DISBROW: I'll give you a tip—cash in your annuities. (*Confronting the designer*) Smeed, I'm a man of few words. Strangle-craft will take your entire output. We'll give you twice as much as your highest present bid.

SMEED: Uh-uh—three times. Plus a nice worldwide advertising campaign in five colors testifying how proud, kindly, adventurous, and warmhearted I am.

FINUCANE: You're a cheap, cold-blooded skinflint and I rue the day we ever crossed the Firth of Forth.

SMEED (*sympathetically*): So do I. What an appalling thing commerce is, scarring this bonnie land with its heaps of slag and setting every man against his neighbor. Ah, weel, we shan't see the end of it in our lifetime, I'll wager. (*He seats himself, dexterously carves off a chunk of haggis with his jackknife, and starts chewing it with relish. As Disbrow, Finucane, and Ermatinger exeunt and Kluckhorn, his face richer by several tics and his hair gone silver, lopes after them—*)

CURTAIN

The Swirling Cape and the Low Bow

If I live to be a hundred years old (a possibility that must have actuarial circles sick with fear), I doubt that I shall ever forget the winter of 1932. It needs no cup of lime-flower tea, macaroon or other Proustian accouterments to help me recall that that was the year I worked on a revue called *Sherry Flip*. It was also the year Rudy Vallee crooned his way to fame in a voice as seductive as mineral oil, the year Douglas MacArthur brilliantly routed the bonus marchers at Anacostia Flats, and the year those sparkling philosophers, Father Coughlin and Howard Scott, bedazzled the lunatic fringe, but all these calamities were trifling compared to *Sherry Flip*. Speaking dispassionately, I would say that the people responsible for that show—and I was as culpable as anyone—set the American theater back a hundred years.

The producer of *Sherry Flip* was a *bon vivant* named Avery Mapes, a onetime yacht broker riding out the depression on a cask of Courvoisier, and its creators were three: Lazlo Firkusny, a Budapest composer, a lyric writer named Lytton Swazey, and myself. Swazey, after years of grinding out special material for those willowy pianists who chant in cocktail bars at nightfall, had teamed up with Firkusny, who wrote popular airs under the pseudonym of Leonard Frayne. Together they confected a valiseful of show tunes, and it was on these, and half a dozen sketches I wrung out of a dry sponge I carried in my head, that the revue was based.

From the first week of rehearsals, it was obvious that the Furies had marked us down. The leading lady fell out with the composer, branded him a Hungarian meat ball, and went into nervous collapse. The comedians, who had made their reputation in burlesque, took a very dim view of my sketches, referring to me disdainfully as Percy Bysshe Shelley. They abandoned the material agreed on and began improvising routines in which they flimflammed a Polack from Scranton with a wallet stuffed with tissue paper, gave impersonations of humorous tramps, and spawned *double-entendres* that made the brain reel. Once embarked, no protestations, no appeals, could curb them; they girded themselves with grotesque rubber feet and boutonnières that spurted water, pursued squealing show-girls into the boxes and thwacked their bottoms with rolled-up newspapers. Their behavior totally unnerved Wigmore, our director, a brilliant man around an Ibsen revival but a newcomer to the revue theatre. The poor man fluttered about in a continual wax, pathetically wringing his hands like Zazu Pitts and endeavoring to assert his authority. In the dance division, there was a similar lack of co-ordination. The production numbers, two portentous ballets of the type informally known in dance circles as "Fire in a Whorehouse," had got away out of hand. Muscle-bound youths stamped about bearing dryads who whinnied in ecstasy, shoals of

58

coryphees fled helter-skelter across the stage, and the choreographer, wild-eyed with exhaustion, sat slumped in the apron, dreaming up new flights of symbolism. It was a holocaust.

We opened in Boston on the eve of Thanksgiving, a season associated from time immemorial with turkeys, and our *première*, I am told, is still spoken of along the Charles. The house curtain did not rise on *Sherry Flip* in the conventional fashion; instead, it billowed out and sank down over the orchestra, perceptibly muffling the overture. The musicians fiddled with might and main underneath, but Firkusny's score was too fragile and lilting to overcome the handicap. The comedy, on the other hand, was exceedingly robust, so much so that the police stepped in the next day and excised four sketches.

The tone of the reviews, by and large, was vengeful. One of the critics felt that we ought to be hunted down with dogs. Another, singling me out as the chief malefactor, stated he would be appeased by nothing short of my heart's blood. For the first time in its twenty-seven years of publication, *Variety* was guilty of a glaring omission. It forgot to review the show at all.

Two nights later, I was emerging from the stage door after a post-mortem when I heard my name called. Turning, I beheld one of our showgirls, a gazelle whose lavish *poitrine* was the despair of the wardrobe mistress and the lodestar of every male in the cast. She was accompanied by a vital, leathery taxpayer with protuberant eyes, opulently clad in a black astrakhan coat sporting a mink collar. His face was screwed around an unlit Partagas which he was savagely chewing into submission.

"My friend would like to know you," said the winsome balloon smuggler. "Meet Georgie Jessel."

"Hello, kid," said her escort hoarsely, seizing me in a paralyzing handclasp. "I've just been out front watching the performance. Does the name of George Armstrong Custer suggest anything to you?"

"Well—er—yes," I said innocently. "Isn't it usually identified with some massacre or other?"

"Indeed it is," he affirmed. "And as I sat there tonight, the walls of the theater receded and it seemed to me that I was back on the Little Big Horn. My friend," he said, his voice solemn, "the handwriting on the wall reads '*Mene mene tekel upharsin.*' Your goose is cooked, the scuppers are awash. Get out of town while there's still time."

"D-don't you see any hope at all?" I asked, trembling.

"Only for the Shuberts," he said inexorably. "They can always flood the auditorium and rent it out to hockey teams. As for yourself, go back to that job at the slaughterhouse. It's not glamorous work, but I can tell from your sketches that you have a career there. *Zei gezünt.*" He wrapped a proprietary arm around his date and swept her off to a hot bird and a cold bottle at Locke-Ober's. Desolate, I watched them go; then, hailing a jitney, I sped to Back Bay and boarded the midnight to New York.

Considering that I spent most of the ensuing decade in Hollywood writing scenarios, an occupation akin to stuffing kapok in mattresses, it was strange that I should not have encountered Jessel. The fact was, however, that he went there infrequently, for his services were not avidly sought by the movie satraps. He held them in rather low regard and his tongue was much too unruly to disguise his contempt. On one occasion, for example, he waspishly interrupted a panegyric someone was delivering about several production geniuses. "Overrated," he snapped. "They could put butter on the film and sell it." Jessel's intimates begged him to be more politic, pointing out that other actors were being given parts he might have had, but the poniard flashed automatically out of the sheath. Typical was the evening he was taken to dine at the home of an M-G-M big wheel who was considering him for a role. Throughout dinner, Jessel was a model of tact and affability. After the walnuts and wine, the party adjourned to the rumpus room for a game of poker. All went well until the host's nine-year-old son, a particularly objectionable lad, entered and began kibitzing. Jessel gnawed his cheroot to ribbons in an effort to contain himself. At length he turned on the producer. "Listen," he rasped. "Why don't you sling that punk across the bridge of your nose and tote him off to bed?" The name of Jessel, needless to add, was conspicuously absent from the cast of characters when the picture was released.

In the amnesty and repatriation that followed the accession of Zanuck I of the Skouras dynasty to the throne of Twentieth Century-Fox, Jessel suddenly confounded the wiseacres and bobbed up as one of the very clan he had derided for years. Whether he became a movie producer through hunger or sheer contrariness is uncertain, but he vanished from Times Square and the lush pastrami beds of the West Forties knew him not. It was whispered along the grapevine that the man was now a Zoroastrian and a food faddist, subsisting entirely on dates, bran, and blintzes made of soybeans, and engaged between times on projects clearly beyond mortal skill, such as translating the prose of Louella Parsons into English. Some even asserted that the real Jessel had succumbed a year before to steam poisoning in a Finnish bath, and that his studio was employing a double to impersonate him.

None of this kit-kit, happily, was true. A few weeks ago, lunching with a friend in the Twentieth Century-Fox commissary, I heard a familiar raucous voice up-raised several tables away. "Sure I like Grossinger's," it was saying, "but let me warn you—if you go up there, be sure and wear sunglasses. You can get snow blindness from the sour cream." It was Jessel, right enough, and nothing had changed but his attire. He was clad in white sharkskin and a chocolate-colored shirt with pale-blue collar and cuffs, wore a coconut-fiber straw encircled by a puggree band, and rotated the inevitable perfecto in his cheek. Our eyes met at the same instant.

"Percy B. Shelley!" he gasped, springing toward me. No Siberian exiles could have exchanged more emotional salutations. "What happened to that revue of yours in Boston? Is it still open?" I revealed that it had closed just prior to its nineteenth anniversary, and he shook his head. "Oh, well, we all have flops," he commiserated. "Say, who's this interesting-looking fellow you're with?"

"Excuse me," I apologized. "Mr. Jessel—John Keats."

"A pleasure, Keats," said Jessel. "I've read your *Ode on a Grecian Urn*. There's a great picture in it; tell your agent to call me. Well," he said, taking me by the arm, "come on, I have to get back to my office. We can talk there."

"But I haven't had my dessert," I protested.

"Quiet," he said under his breath. "You don't want to be seen eating with starvelings—it's bad for you socially in Hollywood." To save Keats's feelings, I told him that since he was jobless, a nonentity, and furthermore strongly suspected of being un-American, he could be of no earthly use to me, and ran after Jessel. Our chance meeting had thrown him into a reminiscent mood; his rhetoric as he expatiated on the early thirties grew more florid by the moment.

"Halcyon days, by Jove," he declaimed. "Gad, I was a picaresque fellow then, another Benvenuto Cellini. It was the day of the swirling cape and the low bow. What madcap escapades, what deeds of high emprise! Albeit my purse was empty, I was ever ready for a duel or a bout with the flagons. One look from Milady's eyes—"

"À propos of that," I put in, "whatever became of the pouter pigeon who introduced us?"

"She married into the peerage," said Jessel impressively. "The Turkish peerage. I sent them a box of halvah for the wedding." His face took on a faraway expression. "What a dainty waist that creature had!" he marveled. "You could span it with your two hands. I spent the winter of '32 spanning it. Here we are." The anteroom of his suite was a smoke-filled chamber resembling a vaudeville booking office. A handful of callers—a lush blonde, a small, ulcerous agent, an insurance canvasser, and a carefully unobtrusive citizen who looked like a dice hustler—greeted Jessel effusively. When they had been disposed of, I rejoined him in his inner sanctum. The memorabilia accumulated in an extensive career as monologist and toastmaster overflowed the walls and furniture; testimonial letters from presidents, banquet scenes, signed cigarette boxes, and posters lay jumbled on his desk amid movie scripts, clippings, and a mountainous correspondence. He was shouting into a phone as I entered.

"How can I open the Santa Anita track that Friday?" he bellowed in anguish. "I have to dedicate a new playground in Tel Aviv the next day! Yes, and emcee the Lambs' Gambol in New York two days after! I tell you, you're killing me, you're ruining my stomach—say no more, Harry, I'll be there." He waved me into a chair, picked up a script, and began intoning over it. "M-m-m. 'Lucy, your eyes are like sesame seeds tonight, sesame and lilies. Anybody who says different is a liar.' 'Oh, Ruskin, don't, don't. What if my husband should come in from his destroyer?' No, that's too bald. The writer's using a javelin instead of a needle." He blue-penciled the speech, and tossing aside the script, swung toward me.

"Why do I do it?" he demanded. "Why does a gifted Thespian, a mummer in the great tradition of Burbage, Macready, and Booth, hock out his brains here for a lousy twenty-five hundred a week when he could be holding audiences spellbound with his magic? I should be playing Strindberg and Shaw in the different world capitals, not vegetating in this cactus-covered suburb!" He smote his breast, taking care not to muss his pocket handkerchief. "When I remember those early days in the theater—the freedom, the bonhomie, the comradeship of those roaches in the dressing rooms! A man could live on nothing at all; I used to pay off my

Chinese laundryman in lichee nuts. Today I've got a mansion overlooking the Pacific, with a library of the world's most expensive classics, a retinue of servants, a cellar of the finest French wines, brandies, and cordials, every luxury money can buy—and yet I'm like a bird in a gilded cage. Sometimes I'm tempted to kick over the whole shebang. If it wasn't for the crushing weight of responsibility, the whole studio on my shoulders—"

"Let someone else carry the load," I advised. "Get away from the artificiality and hypocrisy of Hollywood. Go down to Palm Springs."

"No, it's too primitive, too remote," he said uneasily. "Sometimes it takes the *Hollywood Reporter* a whole day to reach there. Wait a minute, though," he exclaimed. "You gave me an idea. Have you ever been in Catalina? A Garden of Eden—a little fragment of Paradise in an emerald sea! How soon can you be back here?"

"I *am* here," I replied, "and what's more, I've seen Catalina. I went over there in 1938—"

"Look, I haven't got time to listen to travelogues, I'm a busy man," Jessel broke in. "Get some pajamas and a toothbrush, and meet me in an hour at Woloshin's delicatessen. I'll phone down to San Pedro for a boat, we'll pick up a cargo of lox and bagels, and I'll guarantee you a cruise that'll make Magellan look like a farmer."

Naturally, I had no intention of abetting any such harebrained scheme, and I said so. I was still saying so about mid-afternoon as Jessel propelled me down a wharf at San Pedro toward a luxurious motor cruiser, all mahogany and brass, moored alongside it. My companion's innate flair for pageantry had impelled him to

65

outfit us both with yachting caps and binoculars, and he was as salty as one of Joseph C. Lincoln's down-East skippers. The captain of the vessel, a stout foxy-nose in brown gabardine whom I would have cast more accurately as a defaulting bank cashier, welcomed us aboard and begged our indulgence. The starboard Diesel had broken down, but we should be under way within a few minutes. "Take your time, Captain Applejack," said Jessel negligently, stretching out in a chair under the awning. "The others haven't showed up anyway."

"What others?" I asked apprehensively.

"Oh, just some people I invited along to keep us company," he returned. "I figured we might as well play pinochle to while away the trip. How long can you look at the ocean, for God's sake? When you've seen one wave, you've seen 'em all." Before I could invent some plausible excuse to disembark, like a ruptured appendix, our fellow passengers appeared in a peach-colored convertible, clad, to a man, in nylon windbreakers, Bermuda shorts, and berets. They all proved to be either former studio heads who were now agents or former agents who had just become studio heads, and their conversation was so cryptic that it might as well have been in Pawnee. The occasional monosyllables I caught, however, indicated that they were highly suspicious of each other and were only undertaking the voyage as a mark of esteem for Jessel. How profound this was I shortly discovered. One of them deserted the card table at which the rest sat engrossed in the pasteboards and joined me at the rail.

"A great guy, Georgie," he observed emotionally.

"Salt of the earth. You and I'll be lucky to have him read over us when our time comes." I did not quite grasp his meaning and begged for elucidation. "The eulogy," he said impatiently. "Haven't you ever heard him give an address at a burial? Jeez, he'll make you bawl like a baby. I've heard him speak at all kinds of dinners and affairs, but take it from me, nobody can top that boy at a funeral." He was launching into a hushed account of Jessel's eloquence at the interment of some picture notable when the captain reappeared with a long countenance. The engine was hopelessly out of commission, and to further confound our plans, an unexpected tidal wave had submerged Catalina and swallowed it up in the depths of the Pacific. The news acted like digitalis on Jessel, whose mood had been growing progressively more somber at the thought of putting to sea.

"Good riddance," he commented exultantly, as we drove back into Los Angeles. "As a matter of fact, I was opposed to the trip from the start—I only agreed to humor you. Now we can have a good juicy steak and go to the fights." The prospect of watching a number of third-rate pugs maul each other into insensibility in a drafty armory full of cigar smoke was an exhilarating one. Unluckily, I had a prior engagement to dine with two other old friends in the movie colony, Doc Johnson and Jamie Boswell, who were collaborating on a Biblical film at Paramount, and I did not feel I could let them down. The mention of their names drew immediate approbation from Jessel. "A topflight comedy team," he declared. "Strictly with the boffs. Keep this under your hat, but I'm planning a musical about Disraeli, with

Yvonne de Carlo as Queen Victoria, and I'd love to have those boys write it. Tell their agent to call me."

"Right," I said, as we drew up before the Hollywood hotel where I was bivouacked. "Well, it's been a treat seeing you again, old man. By the way, please don't bother to drive me out to the airport when I leave, will you?"

"Of course not," he said warmly. "Now remember, any time you're having a banquet, a christening, a wedding anniversary, or a shower, don't forget Jessel. I've got speeches for all occasions, grave or licentious as the case may be. I can tug at the heartstrings, I can tickle the risibilities, and, if the caterer needs an extra man, I can even carry chairs. *Lox vobiscum*, and give my regards to Broadway." His custom-built wig slid away from the curb and was lost in the stream of traffic. On the sidewalk two urchins were turning handsprings, and somehow they provided a note of poetic justice. After all, nobody could follow Jessel but acrobats.

Swindle Sheet with Blueblood Engrailed, Arrant Fibs Rampant

I promise you I hadn't a clue, when I unfolded my *Times* one recent morning at the bootblack's, that it would contain the most electrifying news to come out of England in a generation—the biggest, indeed, since the relief of Lucknow. As invariably happens after one passes forty, the paper sagged open to the obituary page; I skimmed it quickly to make sure I wasn't listed, and then, having winnowed the theatrical, movie, and book gossip, began reading the paper as every enlightened coward does nowadays, back to front. There, prominently boxed in the second section, was the particular dispatch—terse and devoid of bravura, yet charged with a kind of ragged dignity. "BRITAIN'S INDIGENT LORDS ASK EXPENSE ACCOUNTS," it announced over a London dateline, and went on, "Some peers are too impoverished in the highly taxed present-day welfare state to travel to London and do their duty without pay, the House of Lords was told today. The Upper House, shorn by the last Labor Government of much of its power, was debating its own possible reform. One of its proposals was for giving expense money to those members who do trouble to come to

Westminster. At present the Lords get no salaries and nothing but bare traveling expenses. On an average day no more than one peer in ten is present."

"Well, well!" I exclaimed involuntarily. "It's high time, if you ask me."

"What'd you say?" inquired the bootblack with a start, almost spilling the jonquil-colored dye with which he was defacing my shoes.

"This story about the British peers," I replied. "Poor chaps are practically on the dole—beggars-on-horse-back sort of thing. Pretty ironical situation, what?"

He threw me a sidelong glance, plainly uncertain whether it was safe to commit himself. "You a peer?" he asked cautiously.

"No," I said, "but I do think England's in a hell of a state when your Gloucesters and your Somersets have to get down on their knees and scrounge expense money.

"Yeah, the whole world's falling apart," he said, scratching his ear reflectively with his dauber. "A couple of shmos like you and me, we can't even get up our rent, whereas them dukes and earls and all those other highbinders over there are rolling in dough."

"But they're not," I objected. "Judging from this, they've hardly enough carfare to get from their ancestral seats to London."

"That's what I said—it's all topsy-turvy," he returned. His inflection made it abundantly clear that he was humoring an imbecile. "Look, should I put some new laces in here? These are full of knots."

"I prefer them that way," I said icily, and retired behind the paper. The snub, though momentarily soothing to my ego, cost me dear; in retaliation, he gave me such a flamboyant shine that an old gorgon on the sidewalk mistook me for a minstrel and demanded to know where I was hiding my tambourine.

Fletcherizing the news item subsequently in a more tranquil setting, it occurred to me that while the projected expense accounts might seem a godsend at first glance, they could also be a potential source of embarrassment to the noble lords. No matter how august their lineage, they will eventually have to undergo the scrutiny of, and explain every last deduction to, a corps of income-tax ferrets rated among the keenest in the world. I have been speculating about just how, in these circumstances, one applies the thumbscrews to a man whose title dates back four or five centuries—how, in other words, the British tax inquisitor manages to grovel and browbeat at the same time. Obviously, the best way to find out is to secrete ourselves behind the arras at such an examination. Softly, then, and remember, everything you see or hear henceforth is in strictest confidence.

SCENE: *The office of Simon Auger, an inspector in the review division of the Board of Inland Revenue. A small, cheerless room equipped with the standard instruments of torture—a desk, two chairs, a filing cabinet. As a decorative touch rather than for its psychological effect, someone has hung on the wall a kiboko, or rhinoceros-hide whip. When the curtain rises, Auger, a dyspeptic of forty-odd, is finishing a frugal lunch of Holland Rusk, wheat germ, and parsnips, a copy of* Burke's Peerage *propped up before him. For the most part, his face is expressionless, but occasionally it betrays a wintry smile of the kind observable in barracudas. At length, he sighs deeply, stashes the book in the desk, and, withdrawing a bottle of Lucknow's Instant Relief, downs a spoonful. The phone rings.*

AUGER: Auger here…Who?…Ah, yes. Please ask His Lordship to come in, won't you? (*The door opens to admit Llewellyn Fitzpoultice, ninth Viscount Zeugma. He is in his mid-sixties, ramrod-straight, affects a white cavalry mustache and a buttonhole, and is well dressed to the point of dandyism. Having fortified himself with four brandy-and-sodas at lunch, his complexion—already bronzed by twenty-five years on the Northwest Frontier—glows like an old mahogany sideboard.*)

ZEUGMA (*jauntily*): Afternoon. Hope I'm not terribly late.

AUGER: Not at all. No more than three-quarters of an hour or so.

ZEUGMA: Frightfully sorry. This filthy traffic, you know. I defy anyone to find a cab in Greek Street.

AUGER: Your Lordship was lunching in Soho?

ZEUGMA: Yes, I found a rather decent little place there—Stiletto's. They do you quite well for five guineas—*coquilles St. Jacques*, snails, a tart, and a passable *rosé*. You must try it sometime.

AUGER: I could hardly afford to, at my salary.

ZEUGMA: Between ourselves, I can't either, but the Crown pays for it—ha ha ha. (*blandly*) Necessary business expense in connection with my duties in the Upper House.

AUGER: Indeed. (*He jots down a note.*) By the way, I believe I had the pleasure of meeting a relative of yours about a fortnight ago—the Right Honourable Anthony de Profundis.

ZEUGMA: Wild young cub—Tony. What's the boy been up to?

AUGER: Little matter of evasion and fraud. He was sly, but we specialize in those sly ones—ha ha ha. (*opening a dossier*) Well, let's get on with it, shall we? Your address remains the same, I take it—The Grange, Regurgingham-supra-Mare, Dotards, Broome Abbas, Warwickshire.

ZEUGMA: That's right. But why do you ask?

AUGER: Because your nephew changed his unexpectedly last week, if you follow me.

ZEUGMA: I—I say, it seems dreadfully warm in here. Could we open a window?

AUGER: I'm afraid not. Whoever designed this stage set forgot to include one. However, to resume. According to your return, you made thirty-one trips here from Warwickshire during the last Parliamentary session.

ZEUGMA (*muffled*): Whole avalanche of measures directly affecting my constituency. Crucial decisions. No time for shillyshallying.

AUGER: I have no doubt. Still, in glancing over the minutes of the Upper House I notice Your Lordship didn't speak once in all that period.

ZEUGMA: Blasted committees chained me down. Paperwork from dawn to dark. Closeted with Winnie weeks on end. Barely able to snatch a sandwich.

AUGER: Yes, few of us realize how unselfishly England's public men give of their energy. Notwithstanding, you did find time to squeeze in sixty-three meals, excluding breakfasts, for a total of four hundred fifty-seven pounds thirteen shillings. These were all concerned with legislative matters?

ZEUGMA: Every blessed one. (*spluttering*) Confound it, are you questioning my word?

AUGER: I wouldn't dream of it. I was merely giving you what we call a surface probe—to make certain there was no aura of peculation, as it were. Now suppose we cast an eye at your hotel appropriation. These five-room suites you habitually took at the Dorchester—weren't they a bit grandiose for an overnight stay?

ZEUGMA: By Gad, sir, if you expect me to crawl into some greasy boarding house in Kensington and fry my own kippers—

AUGER: Certainly not, certainly not. One can't conceivably imagine Lady Zeugma in such an atmosphere.

ZEUGMA (*unwarily*): She wasn't with me—er, that is, I was batching it most of the term—

AUGER (*smoothly*): I see. And the rest of the time you shared the accommodations with another legislator?

ZEUGMA: Well—uh—in a way. My staff secretary—or, rather, my secretarial adviser. Mrs. Thistle Fotheringay, of Stoke Poges.

AUGER: Ah, that explains these miscellaneous charges—one hundred eighteen quid for champagne, forty-two pounds ten for caviar, and so on. Naturally, neither you nor Mrs. Fotheringay ever partook of these delicacies paid for by the state?

ZEUGMA (*struggling to dislodge an emery board from his trachea*): N-no, of course not. I just kept 'em on hand for colleagues—for other viscounts, you understand. Haven't touched a drop of bubbly in years. It's death to my liver.

AUGER: Really. Then perhaps you'd care to examine this cutting from a recent issue of the *Tatler*. It shows you and your-ahem-secretarial adviser with upraised champagne glasses, dining at the Bagatelle.

ZEUGMA: Demnition...I say, old man, mind if I pass it along to Mrs. Fotheringay? Women like to preserve sentimental slop like this.

AUGER: I know. That's why I thought of sending it to Lady Zeugma.

ZEUGMA (*agitatedly*): Wait a bit, let's not—We mustn't go off half—By Jove, I've just had an absolutely wizard idea!

AUGER: Amazing how they pop out of nowhere, isn't it?

ZEUGMA: You revenue blokes have some kind of fraternal organization, don't you? I mean where you take the missus to Blackpool, toffee for the kiddies, all that drill?

AUGER: Quite. And if I may anticipate Your Lordship, you'd like to make a small donation to our outing fund.

ZEUGMA: Why, how did you guess?

AUGER: One becomes surprisingly clairvoyant in this line of work.

ZEUGMA: Fancy that. Well, suppose you put me down for about five hundred pounds. Needn't use my name, necessarily. Call it "Compliments of a Friend."

AUGER: Very magnanimous of you, I'm sure.

ZEUGMA: Nonsense—live and let live's my motto. Let sleeping dogs lie, I always say.

AUGER: Yes, and whilst you're raking up proverbs, don't forget there's no fool like an old fool. (*He replaces the dossier in the desk, extends a packaged handkerchief to his illustrious caller.*) Would you care for one of these? Your own seems to be wringing wet.

ZEUGMA (*undone*): Ah, yes, many tax—that is, you're most welcome. Pip-pip. Cheerio. (*He exits, tripping over his stick and ricocheting off the filing cabinet. Auger's eyes crinkle up at the corners and he hums two or three bars of a tuneless little melody. Then, reopening* Burke's Peerage, *he begins nibbling a carrot reflectively as the curtain falls.*)

Come On In, the Liability's Fine

The sunlight was so benign one recent forenoon in the country, and the air laden with such promise of spring, that, on the verge of entering my web to spin a few merchandisable threads, I decided to take a turn about the place and see what catastrophes I could unearth to impair my efficiency. It looked quite unpromising for a while; none of the barn doors had blown off during the night, the ruts in the lane—thitherto as deep as the Union trenches before Vicksburg—had mysteriously filled up by themselves, and the cistern containing our auxiliary supply of rain water had stopped rotting and exuded a fresh, invigorating tang of resin. I was forlornly kicking a terrace wall, in the hope of loosening the stones and embroiling myself in a long, exasperating hassle with masons, when an azure-blue sedan rolled up, backed swiftly around, and splintered the lower branches of a magnolia just coming into flower. A thickset, forceful man of the type who models Shurons in opticians' windows jumped out and cursorily examined the damage. Then, whisking a briefcase from the trunk, he strode toward me with hand extended.

"Howdy," he said, all wind and geniality like a

barber's cat. "Chicanery's my name—Walt Chicanery. I'm with the Hindsight Insurance Company, over in Doylestown. Is the owner here?" I explained that though my clothes belied it, I held the fief, and he chuckled tolerantly to assuage my embarrassment. "You sure fooled me," he said. "I thought you were the handy-man."

"I am," I replied evenly. "I do all the odd jobs, like pruning these trees after people drive over them."

"That's where you're missing a bet, neighbor," he said, stabbing me in the breastbone with his forefinger. "Don't prune 'em—replace 'em. I've got a policy whereby you're fully protected against loss to shrubs, hedges, sedges, vines, pines, creepers, rushes, and ramblers."

"So have I," I disclosed. "I've got any kind of insurance you can name—hailstorm, shipwreck, volcano, libel, frostbite, all of them. I'm even insured against meteors or a rain of red frogs. And now, if you'll excuse me—"

"One moment there," he said patronizingly. "You're pretty cocky, aren't you? Think every possible contingency's provided for, eh? Well, think again. What happens if your bowling ball slips and you break the bones in your companion's foot?"

I knew I should have whistled up my syce and had the fellow beaten off the place with lathees, but the sun felt so good on my back that I let myself be drawn. "The only kind I've ever dropped was a matzo ball," I said, "and I doubt whether it affected Jed Harris's gait. No, sir," I went on, "I don't get involved in those trick mishaps. I'm probably less accident-prone than any man alive. I just sit indoors and do my work, and that's where I'm going now." Entering the outbuilding where I worry, I immersed myself in a sheaf of papers. Simultaneously, Chicanery's hand slid into my field of vision, holding a printed page.

"You owe this to your family, friend," his voice purred into my shoulder. "Just look it over before you send me away."

"What is it?" I asked peevishly.

"A list of typical accidents covered by our new Allstate Comprehensive Personal Liability policy," he said, buttering each word like Svengali. "Go ahead, read it. Go ahead, I dare you." Robbed of my will, I read.

The list was formidable, an encyclopedia of disaster. "A passer-by breaks arm in fall on your icy walk," it intoned. "Your dog bites the deliveryman. Your wife injures a passer-by with her umbrella. Mailman slips on your front step—suffers a concussion. Your child knocks down an elderly person with his sled. Handyman tumbles from your stepladder. Friend suffers a crippling fall on your freshly waxed floor. While hunting, you accidentally shoot another hunter. Your baby-sitter breaks ankle tripping over baby's toy. Neighbor's child falls into trash fire. Your child accidentally hits playmate in eye with ball. Your child runs into bystander with bicycle. You accidentally burn stranger with cigarette. A guest trips over your rug. Your child accidentally sails toy airplane into playmate's face. Your golf drive injures another player. Your back-yard swing breaks, injuring a neighbor's child. A fellow bus passenger trips over your suitcase or package. Baseball bat slips from your son's hands—hurtles into spectator's face. Your trash fire spreads to a neighbor's home. Your child accidentally breaks plate-glass window. Your cat claws visitor's expensive fur coat."

I looked up at Chicanery, who, while I was absorbed, had flipped open my checkbook and was examining the balance with amused contempt, and handed back the prospectus. "Listen, this is all very well for schlemiels," I said, "but I repeat—none of that stuff happens to yours truly. I've crisscrossed the ruddy globe, waded knee-deep in malarial swamps, slept cheek by jowl with hamadryads, shared my last catty of rice with head-hunters, and never even had a nosebleed. You're barking up the wrong tree, Tuan. Good day."

"Ta-ta," he said, without tensing a muscle. "Say, what's that whistling I hear down on your porch? A bird?" I admitted that I own a rather gifted myna acquired in Thailand, who speaks idiomatic Siamese, Chinese, and English, and who allows nobody but me to gentle him. "You don't say," he marveled. "What's he do when your guests reach into his cage?"

"Who—Tong Cha?" I asked carelessly. "Oh, he generally goes for their eyes. He thinks they're grapes."

"Be a shame to shell out fifty thousand damages for a grape," observed Chicanery with a yawn. "A party over here in Chalfont got hooked that way. His rooster bit off a little boy's nose. Time the courts finished with him, the poor devil was on relief."

"B-but Tong Cha wouldn't hurt anyone intentionally," I said, suddenly agitated. "I mean, basically he's sweet—he's just playful, full of beans—"

"Well, maybe he can explain that to the jury," said Chicanery. "Or maybe you'll be lucky enough to get a Siamese judge. Otherwise, you're going byebye with an iron ball soldered to your leg, as sure as you're born."

"Er—how much did you say that policy was?" I inquired, moistening my lips. "I might be able to swing it after all. I don't really need a bridge on these molars; I can chew on the other side."

"Sure you can," the agent agreed sympathetically. "Your cheeks are bound to cave in sooner or later, no matter what you do. Now, here's the deal." Within twenty minutes, and to the accompaniment of a spate of actuarial jargon I only half understood, I was formally indemnified against a host of actionable casualties that might befall me or my dependents, whether human or members of the brute creation.

As Chicanery finished ticking off the complex provisions, he caught himself abruptly. "Danged if I haven't forgot the drowning clause," he exclaimed. "That's what comes of somebody jabbering in your ear."

"There's no water on this place," I objected. "Just the little creek you drove through in the lane. You couldn't drown a chipmunk in that."

"Hunh, that's what Dr. Bundy over at Keller's Church thought," rejoined Chicanery. "His wife's brother came home one night drunk as a boiled owl, fell in the brook, and goodbye Charlie. Widow collected seventy-four grand and poor Bundy blew his brains out. I don't want you coming around with a beef if it happens to you."

"O.K., O.K.," I said impatiently. "Is the policy in effect from now on?"

"Yup, soon as your check clears," he said. "Personally, I always recommend paying cash so you get immediate protection." I at once yielded up what

81

currency I had in my clothes, then repaired to the house and levied on the kitchen funds, and finally amassed the premium, a good share of it in pennies. Chicanery stowed it away in his poke and, teetering back in my mid-Victorian swivel chair, beamed paternally at me.

"Someday you'll bless me for this," he declared. "A stitch in time—" There was a fearful crack of wood and metal, the chair crumbled into matchwood, and Chicanery catapulted backward, describing the figure known among movie stunt men as the Hundred and Eight. In landing, he unfortunately dislodged a pile of atlases and gazetteers, which rained down on him like building blocks and almost hid him from view. I sprang up and flung aside the sailing directions for Macassar Strait and the copy of *Menaboni's Birds* resting on his head. His face had gone the color of an old Irish towel and he was breathing heavily through his mouth.

"Are you all right?" I demanded, seizing his shoulders and shaking him vigorously. Two years as a biology major, plus wide reading of illustrated hygiene magazines along Sixth Avenue, have taught me that in possible concussions the patient should be stimulated to keep the circulation brisk.

Chicanery opened his eyes and goggled about stupidly. "Where am I?" he murmured.

"Right here in the Pennsylvania Dutch country, about nine miles from Riegelsville," I assured him, endeavoring to keep my voice buoyant. "Is anything hurting you? Can you twist your neck?" With a grunt, he shook me off and clambered to his feet. A normal healthy flush was momentarily replacing his pallor. He looked fit as a fighting cock, and I said so.

"Leave that up to my doctor," he snapped, dusting off his pants. "It could be internal injuries, like as not. Whatever it is, we can settle it between us. You won't have to go to court."

I had some difficulty in enunciating clearly, but I made my point at last. "You just sold me a policy that covered this type of accident!" I bellowed. "I thought you were sincere! *I* was sincere! Now you tell me—"

"Look, Mister," said Chicanery, his eyeballs shrinking to two bits of flint. "No use trying to bluster your way out of it. If you wanted protection against falls sustained from furniture, you should have specified. That chair is a death-trap, and you could be jailed for using it. You'll hear from my lawyer." He sailed out, slamming the door with such force that a loose slate pitched off the roof and struck him between the shoulder blades. Through the window, I saw him sink to his knees in a position of deep meditation, like a Buddhist monk. Then he arose heavily and, making a notation on a pad, tottered to his car. Five seconds later, it disappeared over the brow of the hill, trailing a flowering magnolia from its bumper. I haven't heard a rumble out of him since, but one of these days my heirs and assigns will undoubtedly receive a bulky envelope with a Doylestown postmark. I must leave word behind to forward it on to Singapore.

Sorry—No Phone or Mail Orders

When a perfume called Chaqueneau-K was launched a couple of seasons ago with a campaign designed to prevent women from buying it, there was a lot of headshaking around the Advertising Club of New York, and more than one scarlet-faced old member gloomily prophesied, over his gin-and-French, the death of retailing. "Damn it all, sir, it won't go down," the Tories sputtered. "Bullyrag the consumer, deride him if you will, but you can't dispense with the beggar altogether. Someone's got to move the bloody stuff off the shelves." The forebodings were, as it turned out, groundless; ladies bent on achieving the unattainable cozened their menfolk into procuring it for them, and today any *femme soignée* would consider herself *vieux jeu* without a flacon of Chaqueneau-K in her *parfumoir*. (Well, almost any *femme soignée*.) Quite recently, the technique has been gaining ground among other storekeepers, notably Macy's and a men's-apparel firm in Baltimore named Lebow Brothers. The former's announcement of a fur sale, while not out-and-out preventive advertising, narrowed down the market to a mere handful of the élite: "Just 10 very precious natural ranch mink cape stoles go on sale tomorrow—$377. Hard to believe a lustrous, deeply piled natural ranch mink cape stole could cost so little? It's true true true at Macy's tomorrow! Just 10 very lucky women will get ten very precious mink buys," etc., etc. Lebow Brothers, apostrophizing a men's cashmere jacket in the pages of *Vogue*, was even more dickty: "Cashmiracle… so rare each coat is registered. Woven by the famous Worumbo Mill. This miracle in cashmere makes a truly proud possession. The finest underdown of 20 goats makes one jacket. In Oyster White, Moonlight Blue, Mulberry, Bamboo." The text opens a whole host of nerve-tingling possibilities, such as the hijacking by goniffs of an armored car laden with Cashmiracles, or the crisis at Worumbo when, in the course of looming a jacket for some noted coxcomb like Danton Walker, one of his twenty sacrificial goats is found to possess no underdown. The temptation to substitute the hair of a Bedlington terrier or a yak might understandably arise, though I imagine Worumbo's blenders are incorruptible—and heavily bonded, to boot. In which case, of course, the suspense would stem from some rival columnist, say Ed Sullivan or Barry Gray, attempting to suborn a blender into using the ersatz to discredit Walker. In short, the dramatic complications could be hilarious, especially if you added a Shakespearean holocaust and killed off all the protagonists in the end.

The upshot of this constricted merchandising, foreseeably, is that the average shopper may soon be frozen out of the picture, and, unless he has a controlling interest in the United States Gypsum Corporation, a listing in *Debrett*, and a membership in the jockey Club of France, will be unable to purchase the ordinary necessities of life. The easiest way to appreciate his plight, perhaps, is to follow an exemplar named Leo Champollion, whose garter has snapped while crossing against a light, into a haberdashery in the East Fifties. The establishment, deeply carpeted and indirectly lit, has no vulgar fixtures like showcases or spittoons to identify it as an outfitter's; given another urn or two, it could be a mortuary or a gastroenterologist's waiting room. As Champollion enters in a crouching position, tugging at his socks, Elphinstone, a lard-faced salesman, finishes pinning a camellia in his lapel and approaches languidly.

ELPHINSTONE (*from across a gulf*): You wished—?

CHAMPOLLION: I busted a garter just now—the elastic's all shot.

ELPHINSTONE: Soddy, we don't vulcanize old rubber. There's a garage over on Second Avenue that may conceivably aid you.

CHAMPOLLION: Aw heck, she's not worth fixing. I'll take a new pair.

ELPHINSTONE (*suavely*): Indeed? May I have your name, please?

CHAMPOLLION: Why—er—Champollion. But what difference does it make? I just want an inexpensive—

ELPHINSTONE: Champollion, eh? Any relative of the distinguished Egyptologist?

CHAMPOLLION: No-o-o, not as I know it. I'm with the Cattaraugus Yeast Company, in the enzyme division.

ELPHINSTONE: I see. And who recommended you to us?

CHAMPOLLION: Nobody. I happened to look up and

see your sign "Cravatoor."

ELPHINSTONE: You mean you haven't been previously introduced or filed application to enroll as a customer?

CHAMPOLLION: I—I didn't know you had to.

ELPHINSTONE: My dear fellow, the clientele of this shop comprises some of the biggest gazebos in the country. If we were to bother with every whipper-snapper who blunders in off the street, how long do you think we'd stay in business?

CHAMPOLLION (*piteously*): But I can't walk around this way, like a college boy! How can I call on the prospects with my sock hanging down?

ELPHINSTONE: That's your headache. Mine is to safeguard the stock so that pikers won't sneak in and buy it out from under our nose. Good day.

CHAMPOLLION: Look, I'll pay double the usual price! (*His voice becomes incoherent.*) I'm a family man, with two little chiggers—I mean two little nippers—

ELPHINSTONE (*relenting*): Well, I'll make an exception this time, but if it ever leaks out, it'll cost me my job.

CHAMPOLLION: I won't tell anybody—honest I won't. I'll say I stole them.

ELPHINSTONE: All right, then, sit down and I'll take your measurements. (*Pulls on surgical gloves.*) Now, hoist up your trousers; I don't want to get these septic …Hmm, that's a pretty scrawny-looking calf you've got there.

CHAMPOLLION: It's wiry, though. I used to beat everybody at stickball.

ELPHINSTONE: Well, you could have done with a bit of polo. Let's see, we might anchor a catch here—

CHAMPOLLION (*diffidently*): Look, wouldn't a regular-sized garter fit me? You know, just ordinary ones—maroon or navy blue. There don't have to be those naked girls on the webbing.

ELPHINSTONE: It isn't a question of size, and anyway, when the time comes *we'll* decide what pattern is best on you. What I'm concerned with now is the contour of your leg so I can fill out my sculptor's report.

CHAMPOLLION: Hanh? What's that for?

ELPHINSTONE: To aid him in modeling the garter, man. (*Impatiently*) Don't you understand? Each pair is sculptured to the wearer's individual requirements by an artist specially commissioned for the task. In your case, it could be one of the academicians, like Paul Manship or Wheeler Williams, if your knees aren't too knobby.

CHAMPOLLION: Wh–what if they are?

ELPHINSTONE: Ah, then we'd have to call in an abstractionist—Henry Moore or Calder. Naturally, their fees are higher and you'd have to sustain the cable charges should we send your specifications abroad.

CHAMPOLLION (*uneasily*): I wasn't figuring on too much expense, to tell you the truth.

ELPHINSTONE: Possibly not, but you don't realize the trouble involved. First, we have to make a plaster-of-Paris form of your shinbone, then a mockup in laminated wood, which is baked under pressure, sanitized, and aged. This guides the sculptor so he can rough out his cast.

CHAMPOLLION: But I can't wear stone garters! I have to be on my feet all day.

ELPHINSTONE: We wouldn't allow you to. They're

simply the matrix from which we execute your personalized accessory in a variety of materials. Here's a swatch to give you an idea. This one, as you see, simulates pickled pine.

CHAMPOLLION: What's that one—plastic?

ELPHINSTONE: No, it only simulates plastic; it's infinitely more costly. Here's one in a fabric so nearly resembling human flesh that customers frequently can't find their garters once they're on.

CHAMPOLLION: Is that good?

ELPHINSTONE (*stiffly*): We're not here to answer metaphysical questions, Mr. Champollion. We're here to not sell merchandise.

CHAMPOLLION: I was only asking. I didn't mean to sound fresh. (*Peering at another sample*) Say, isn't this what I've got on?

ELPHINSTONE: Hardly. That's what we call *trompe-l'oeil*. It may look like worn-out elastic, but it's not elastic at all. It's grypton, the sleaziest plastic known.

CHAMPOLLION: Jeekers, you can't keep up with science nowadays, can you?

ELPHINSTONE (*with Olympian amusement*): No. I suppose it must be rather confusing for a layman. Well, let's start with the mold—

CHAMPOLLION: Uh—I was wondering—couldn't you advance me a pair of garters just for the time being, till I get back to Yonkers?

ELPHINSTONE: Quite impossible. Our vaults close at three.

CHAMPOLLION (*supplicatory*): Or even a piece of twine, so's I could finish my calls. I'd send it back by messenger.

ELPHINSTONE: No, but in view of the circumstances, I'll stretch a point and expedite the psychological quiz. (*Flicks the switch of a Dictograph concealed in an urn.*) Elphinstone to Glintenkamp. Will you be good enough to come in here, Doctor? (*Before Champollion's motor apparatus can function, a dynamic young man enters from rear. He wears a speculum and a physician's smock improvised from an old flour sack, on the back of which is visible, in faded blue letters, the legend "Ceresota—Best by Test."*)

GLINTENKAMP: Eligibility prognosis?

ELPHINSTONE: If you please. Solvency dubious, physique zero minus four.

CHAMPOLLION (*eyes rolling affrightedly*): I can't stay any longer. My boss'll have a connip—

GLINTENKAMP: Now, now, nobody's going to hurt you. Just look at these cards and tell us what the various shapes suggest to you. Come on.

CHAMPOLLION: S-someone spilled gravy on it. Juice of some kind.

GLINTENKAMP: No, no, they're blots of ink. Try to concentrate, now don't they remind you of anything?

CHAMPOLLION: Well, the top part there...um...that could be a face, a man's profile.

GLENTENKAMP: Anyone you know?

CHAMPOLLION: Uh-uh. Wait a minute, though. It's a little like Mr. Bastinado.

GLINTENKAMP: Your boss?

CHAMPOLLION: No, a credit manager up our way. He works for the Procrustes Finance people.

GLINTENKAMP (*significantly*): I see. Go ahead, keep trying.

CHAMPOLLION: This one on the side looks like— well, like pencils in a cup.

GLINTENKAMP: That'll do. (*To Elphinstone*) Impoverishment fixation. Strictly a vag. Boost him.

CHAMPOLLION (*anxiously*): Did I pass? Am I going to get the garters?

ELPHINSTONE: Just close your flap and pretend to be a special-delivery letter. You're practically in Yonkers. (*As one man, he and Glintenkamp sweep up Champollion, propel him to the door, and toss him into oblivion.*)

GLINTENKAMP (*consulting his watch*): Well, five o'clock. The end of a perfect day.

ELPHINSTONE: Yep, all the goods intact and not a cent in the register. I tell you, Doc, this business is going places. Another year like this and we'll be moving over onto the Avenue. (*Radiant, the two of them exit to prepare a banner advertisement for* Vogue *celebrating their collapse.*)

CURTAIN

Don't Tell Me, Pretty Gypsy

When one exercises his inalienable right to line a bureau drawer with newspaper on a humid day and deposit in it a couple of freshly ironed shirts, it's a cinch the resultant decalcomania on his bosom will eventually elicit comment from some busybody or other. I was at my optician's the other morning, myopically waiting for him to finish soldering the bridge of my glasses, when he broke off his labors and leaned closer.

"Well," he said with the relish people invariably evince in reporting a theatrical debacle, "I see where the New York *Post* didn't exactly rave over that show down on Second Avenue, *Girl of My Dream.*"

"Where'd you see that?" I asked.

"On your shirt," he replied pleasantly. "Like me to read it to you?" He lifted aside my cravat for a better view and removed from his tongue a particle of solder that impeded his diction. "'Nobody, I suspect, has gotten, or is going to get, very excited about the plot of the Yiddish musical, *Girl of My Dream*, closing the season for Edmund Zayenda and Irving Jacobson at the Second Avenue Theater this weekend,'" he read. "'The story of the air pilot lost at sea, who turns up as a member of a gypsy band with amnesia, is pretty old hat.' The next part is kind of wrinkled from your tie clasp, but he says down here, '*Girl of My Dream* is not going to start any innovations in the Yiddish theater.'"

"Well, it's only one man's opinion," I returned shortly, tucking the review back into my waistband. "The idea sounds breezy enough to me."

"Me, too," he concurred. "Say, how come you stenciled that on your shirt front? You a friend of the critic?"

"No, he pays me to do it," I said. "I'm a sandwich man for the drama critics. Yesterday I had on a plug for Brooks Atkinson." The novelty of this so overwhelmed him that I finally had to abandon the glasses and feel my way home. As I was reversing the shirt, though, I began to ponder the summary of the plot, and it struck me again as being most cavalier. I felt that the idea of a shipwrecked airman becoming a member of a gypsy band with amnesia, far from being démodé, could make a corking musical if handled right. (That is, if only the pilot had amnesia; if the whole band had it, as the *Post* implied, the device might be a shade cumbersome.) After all, what was so world-shaking about the premise of a romance between a Navy nurse and a French colonial resident, or an English governess and a Siamese potentate? Yet each of these was the basis of a smash: *Hit the Deck* and *Chu Chin Chow*. In other words, the librettist desirous of fashioning a silk purse can use any sow's ear that presents itself, and, buoyed up by this maxim, I have been formulating a tight, workable outline that grows naturally out of the original situation. Inasmuch as the Second Avenue production, written by Joseph Rumshinsky and William Siegel, snapped shut without my seeing it, any resemblance between our two efforts is, of course, illusory; in fact, I have deliberately eschewed all standard motifs like tambourines, horse thievery, and hidden birthmarks to avoid possible conflict. Nothing could be fairer than that.

Our opening scene must, to my way of thinking, have a nautical tang, with a locale off the Balkan coast wherever gypsies tend to forgather—Dalmatia, let us say. On the horizon, the famous blue cliffs of Dalmatia rise sheer, and at center stage, half dead from exposure to the cruel Dalmatian sun, lies Speed Wintringham on an inflated rubber raft. From his rather incoherent soliloquy—a futuristic background of woodwinds and strings suggests that the exposition may really be going on in his head—we gather that he remembers bailing out of his plane but naught else. In short, a good-looking, brawny young American flier, temporarily discombobulated but not medically certifiable. Just as his hopes of rescue are dwindling, a felucca manned by gypsies appears. Their presence in these waters—or, indeed, in any waters—may take a bit of justification, as gypsies are not notably a seafaring folk; however, we weave in some skillful allusion or other to their inherent restlessness, their hatred of fetters, and package it in a ringing chorale wherein they joyously pound their canisters on the gunwales, and the audience won't have time to speculate. You never let grass grow under your feet on such occasions. In a musical I once helped confect that perished in Philadelphia, the actors paused to explain how some Thracian hoplites had strayed into Dolores Gray's bedroom. When they looked up, they had an unobstructed view of the interior of the Erlanger Theatre clear back to Chadds Ford. Even the candy concessionaires had vanished.

Anyhow, hanging over the ship's rail, and a veritable orchid among thistles, is a lovely ash-blond vision named Darleen, whose blouse continually slips off her shoulders—a good comedy touch and highly authentic costumewise in a nomad lass. Darleen is, supposedly, the daughter of the gypsy chieftain, Stanislas, but in the confusion of hauling Speed aboard, chafing his wrists, and reviving him with fiery Dalmatian brandy we plant that there is something fishy about the girl's actual origin. I mean just a glancing reference, like spurts of revulsion at her companions' mentality and table manners, little signs of fastidiousness that will pay off plotwise later on. One hinge at Speed and, needless to say, Darleen falls. She sings "My Heart Floats Up," a ballad that subtly combines love's yearning with the sea, our common mother. While not wedded to the lyric that follows, I believe it will serve as a beacon:

> Out where the whelks and starfish crawl,
> Amid the sea wrack and the combers,
> I found a pearl in my deep-sea haul
> That spells one of Cupid's diplomas.
> My heart floats up when I discern
> A castaway so taciturn.
> I'll nurse and tend you, mend you, bend you,
> Rend you, send you from my orbit nevermore.

Speed, as yet, is too bushed to return Darleen's love, and hovers between life and death (it might be preferable, for the sake of more squeamish patrons, to have him hover offstage), but meanwhile Zilboor, a darkly handsome young gypsy who has long craved the girl, starts resenting the newcomer and musically plots his destruction. This is an ideal opportunity for an imaginative dream sequence in which Zilboor envisions himself bowstringing Speed and being hounded by the devils of remorse. Actually, the rivalry theme is an ingenious subterfuge on our part, because once it is built up, we never refer to it again. The next scene introduces a distinct change of pace. The setting is present-day New York—an exclusive discount house on West Forty-seventh Street, one of those establishments that sell toasters, radios, waffle irons, and similar appliances, where Gotham's socially elect converge to exchange gossip and seek bargains. Speed's mother, a grande dame descended from early Dutch patroons, has come here to buy an egg timer, and encounters a bridge friend she has not seen for years. Their conversation reveals that Speed, only heir to a great real-estate fortune and betrothed to Bibi Witherspoon, a leading débutante, tired of his playboy existence a few months before and took a job with an obscure Greek airline. Mrs. Wintringham voices fears for his safety, knowing that he flies one of the world's most treacherous routes, the Dalmatian run. She wishes he would return home, wed Bibi, and head up his father's manifold realty ventures. What she doesn't suspect is that Speed is in Manhattan at this very moment. The gypsies, chafing under tyranny, have migrated thither and are encamped in a store on Eighth Avenue. While Darleen tells fortunes and tenderly ministers to Speed, still convalescent on a pallet in the back room, Stanislas and the others strive to gain a foothold in the New World by marking cards, playing the handkerchief switch, and glomming laundry off the lines. A good contrast here between a primitive, unspoiled people and the staccato dynamism of the metropolis engulfing them. It can be musically underlined or not, as the case may be.

The plot now goes into high gear. Bud Zapotecky, a fledgling theatrical agent, has been combing the town for a blond gypsy singer to star in a forthcoming ice show. Frustrated at every turn, he is wending his melancholy way homeward down Eighth Avenue—we have established that he lives on Varick Street—when he bears Darleen's glorious soprano issuing from the store. Her glowing beauty surpasses his anticipations; this is the girl for the role. What is more, he falls desperately, hopelessly in love with her, and declares it in a number I provisionally call "You're the Answer to My Unremitting Quest." The words are flexible enough to be rearranged in almost any way required:

> Cortez sought everywhere for gold,
> And Peary the Pole in unimaginable cold,
> Ehrlich the pallid spirochete unfroze,
> And I found you under my very nose.
> Through deepest gloom, like Speke and Mungo Park,
> I've followed your chimera in the dark.
> No trophy could compare with you, I
>   want to share my lair with you,
> Dispel my every care with you and then let down my hair
>   with you,
> My lovely meadow lark.

Darleen, seizing on a mummer's career as a means of

procuring Speed the delicacies he needs to get well (his character, incidentally, seems to be developing into the most valetudinarian in the history of show business), gives up her palmistry and begins rehearsals. As a result, the gypsies fall into arrears on their rent, and the landlord—i.e., Speed's own father—hastens down to evict them. The sight of Mr. Wintringham instantly restores his son's memory, but the joyful reunion curdles when the elder learns that the boy worships Darleen. Threatening to disinherit him if he does not accede, he hales Speed off to marry Bibi Witherspoon, and Act I ends with Darleen, brokenhearted, sobbing in her agent's arms. Thus far, it must be admitted, Speed's part in the story has consisted mainly of hollow groans, and it may not be easy to find an actor of the first magnitude to play him. We might have to draw on someone of the second, or even cut the part altogether, if this can be done without weakening the structure.

Time has wrought substantial changes by the opening of Act II. Overnight, Darleen's ethereal loveliness has captivated blasé playgoers, and she is ensconced as the reigning star of Broadway—a bitter triumph, for the personable young birdman remains ever verdant in her thoughts. A poignant scene this, in her dressing room, as she stares into a mirror and sings "I Have a Plenitude of Everything but You," a panorama of lovers' tribulations through the ages. Deftly woven into the lyric are famous attachments paralleling hers, such as those of Jubilee Jim Fisk and Josie Mansfield, Blazes Boylan and Molly Bloom, Swann and Odette, etc. As for Bud Zapotecky, now the ranking agent of theaterdom and still her ardent slave, Darleen cannot bring herself to accept him, fearing he loves her merely for her commissions. She intimates this to him musically that evening in "Is It the Girl or the Client You Love?" when they dine vis-à-vis at an ace nitery. The mood of the song is lightly mocking, but underneath runs a vein of seriousness:

> Ten per cent of me is yours,
> By legal ties we're bound,
> Yet though the repetition of it bores,
> An ounce is but a fraction of a pound.
> I'll pay my debt of gratitude,
> I'll speak of you with all esteem,
> To you I owe my clothes and food,
> But love? You must not dream this dream.

Hence, by cleverly blending our story elements we have now brought about an impasse that will require ingenuity aplenty to resolve. Zapotecky provides the key. Realizing he stands between Darleen's happiness, he goes to Bibi Witherspoon, who he has reason to believe nurses ambitions of becoming a nightclub songstress, and proposes to her. Avid for success, she breaks her engagement to Speed, and, without quite knowing how it happened—though *we* know—the lovers are reunited. Then, thunderclapwise, comes the revelation of Darleen's birthright that smooths the path to marriage. Stanislas, stabbed in a gypsy fray offscene, confesses she is not his child but the daughter of a Milwaukee flour titan, abducted from the latter's yacht in the Adriatic. The Wintringhams extend their heartfelt blessing to the nuptials, and the curtain falls on a glittering wedding reception at which gypsies rub elbows with the *haut monde*.

Of course, a bare outline can't possibly convey the effervescence and sparkle the show would have opening night; there are myriad opportunities for boffs—for instance, in a scene where some Thracian hoplites get into Darleen's bedroom by mistake. What it needs now is sponsorship—a group of investors willing to gamble forty or fifty thousand to subsidize one while he works out the intricacies. If I were to accept the task—mind you, I'm not saying I would, unless I had the money in five-dollar bills, say—I'd fly over to the Dalmatian coast, spend a month or two trying to get the feel of the thing, and then keep right on going. I don't think the script ought to be readied for next season anyway. Better to skip a year or two, until the critical fraternity begins hungering for a good gypsy musical. You'll get intimations of it when the time is ripe. Just keep an eye on the drama columns—or, better still, my shirt.

CLOUDLAND REVISITED:
By the Waters of Razz-Ma-Tazz

Toward the end of 1920, or just about the time the fencing foils on my bedroom wall were yielding to sepia portraits of Blanche Sweet and Carol Dempster, I became briefly enamoured of a Rhode Island schoolmate named, if memory serves, Celia Cahoon. Together with a dozen other unemployables that semester, Miss Cahoon and I were retracing Xenophon's footsteps to the sea, and as we toiled our daily twenty parasangs over the stony Mesopotamian plain, leaving a wake of dead and dying gerunds, I felt myself involuntarily succumbing to her spell. Though hardly the comeliest girl in the class, Celia possessed a figure so voluptuous that it addled every male within a radius of fifty feet. Whenever she was called on to recite, chairs began to scrape, pencils rolled off the desks, people upset ink on their pants, and the quickened exhalations formed a steam that fogged the windows. In her senior year at Classical High, Celia undoubtedly came in for more accidental jostling in corridor and lunchroom than anyone prior to Sophia Loren.

It was, therefore, with as much exultation as though I had been singled out of the ranks by Catherine of

Russia that I mounted the stoop of the Cahoon residence one December evening, painstakingly groomed for the soirée Celia had bidden me to. In both dress and deportment, I was patterning myself after Wallace Reid, the brightest star in my movie galaxy; I wore a yellow butterfly bow and a wasp-waisted tweed suit with globular leather buttons, my hair (modishly parted in the middle) exuded a paralyzing scent of bay rum, and my swagger was debonair to the point where I was having trouble retaining my balance. Whom Celia was impersonating at the moment I have no idea, but I remember bee-stung lips pouting out of a heavy mask of rice powder, and a hairdress of those unlovely puffs we used to call "cootie garages," accentuated by a wicked spit curl. The lights in the parlor were low, and another couple, also from our class, was executing a vertiginous tango to "La Veeda." While Celia hastened to fetch me a glass of some ghastly punch made of muscatel and sliced oranges, I adopted a *dégagé* pose on the arm of a Morris chair and, stifling a well-bred yawn, covertly studied my surroundings. The family's taste in art was plainly cultivated; in addition to the standard chromo of Landseer's "Dignity and Impudence," there was a side elevation of a pearly nude with red hair by Henner and half a dozen etchings by Anders Zorn. Their library also hinted at a wide intellectual horizon, ranging from fluff by Peter B. Kyne and James Oliver Curwood to substantial works by John Spargo and Brand Whitlock.

"Now, don't be an old bookworm," said Celia effervescently, seizing my wrist. "Come on, slowpoke, let's shake a tibia!" To be in close proximity to the figure

I had so long admired was an exhilarating experience, and when my hostess coyly disclosed that her folks would not be home until midmorning, I figured I had hit the mother lode. As the punch took effect, the pace grew markedly giddier; there was a rare amount of tickling and squealing, and the ladies had frequent recourse to the lipstick that dangled from the chain of the floor lamp—a fribble that I pretended to sneer at but that actually impressed me as the acme of sophistication. But whatever the romp I contemplated in the Elysian fields, the gods had ordained otherwise. Made overconfident by wine, I decided to re-enact an adagio Wallace Reid had performed in his latest vehicle, *The Dancin' Fool*. I clasped Celia in a cheek-to-cheek embrace and, to the cadences of Coon-Sanders and their Blackhawk orchestra, began a series of improvised pirouettes in the style known as the balconade. Just as we were completing a dizzying backward dip, my partner's heel caught in the green plush portieres suspended from an archway, and we fell heavily, demolishing a rubber plant and the lower panel of a Globe-Wernicke bookcase. At that instant, the door opened and two old crabs by the name of Cahoon entered. They had unexpectedly altered their plans, and, it shortly transpired, my own.

Normally, nothing could have persuaded me to revive such painful memories, but they crowded in pell-mell to a screening I was granted recently, by the Museum of Modern Art, of this very Wallace Reid classic. Like *The Roaring Road* and *Excuse My Dust*, his automotive sagas of the same epoch, *The Dancin' Fool* was a breezy success story, altogether synthetic and as devoid of motivation as Happy Hooligan. Its leading man, for all his dazzle, was probably the least gifted actor of the century—a sizable achievement in a medium that begot Nelson Eddy, Henry Wilcoxon, and Mario Lanza. At the risk of alienating readers wholesale, I submit a précis of the plot, but it must be understood that I act merely as an intermediary, or vector. The management will not be responsible for any lost illusions, heartbreak, or ennui poisoning.

The Jones Jug Company, the setting of Wally's initial exploits, is an old-fashioned pottery concern headed by his Uncle Enoch (Raymond Hatton), a stereotyped curmudgeon who bitterly resents progress. Into this milieu bounces Reid, cast as a fresh young hayseed named Sylvester Tibble (or Ves Tibble, naturally), seeking a business career. Given the post of office boy, he at once pantomimes cyclonic energy, raising clouds of dust with his broom, ruffling the bookkeeper's wig, scoffing at the filing system, and generally roiling his elders. After dusk, his uncontrollable zest for dancing leads him into a basement cabaret whose songstress, Junie Budd (Bebe Daniels), seeks his protection from a masher. Wally flattens the offender, and Junie, captivated by his dimples, invites him to her mother's boarding house and offers to coach him in ballroom technique. "You've got regular rattleboxes in your feet," she declares, obviously unaware of a pair that were making every cake-eater in Rhode Island drool with envy. In no time at all—one lap dissolve, in fact—the couple have blossomed out as a dance team in the cabaret, doing a Dutch specialty at their *première* that establishes new frontiers in bathos. Among the patrons, it just so happens is a wealthy pottery tycoon named Harkins (Tully Marshall), who is established as avid to gain control of the Jones Jug Company's clay pit, a circumstance without burning relevance to the floor show but that provides a yeast for future villainy. Wally and Junie now reappear in an apache number so sensational, presumably, that a rival café owner signs them up at two hundred a week, whereupon they run home to apprise Junie's mother of their success and Wally proposes to her. To Junie, that is, not her mother, although actually it wouldn't have made much difference. By this point in the proceedings, it was crystal-clear to me that the engineer was drunk in the cab, the locomotive out of control, and the switches wide-open.

At the Jones Jug Company, where our hero continues as office boy while dancing professionally at night—a movie premise as plausible as most of them—the firm's drummer, a blow-hard and wineskin, returns from a sales trip and angrily resigns when Wally questions his expense account. Thereupon in a comic routine that has begun to lose some of its sizzle with repetition, Uncle Enoch upbraids his nephew for exceeding authority, fires him summarily and hires him back at once. Disclosed next are Junie and Wally at their cabaret that evening, clad in leopard skins and presenting a divertissement billed as "Antediluvian Antics," which it would be flattery to describe as the nadir of choreography in our time. Nonetheless Harkins (who apparently uses the crib as his headquarters) applauds it vociferously from ringside and invites Wally to his table. There the latter overhears him confide to a subordinate, "The way to get old Jones's business is to buy up his pottery and I believe he'd sell out for a dollar." Sensing the machinations that threaten his uncle, Wally racks his brain for some novelty that might stimulate sales, and evolves a repulsive line of containers with human faces he calls B–Jones B–Jugs. Uncle Enoch, betraying the one flicker of taste visible anywhere in the picture, quite properly refuses to countenance them, but, to rid himself of Wally's paranoid schemes, permits him to take over as traveling salesman. When Junie discovers her partner has doffed his leotards for commerce she breaks their engagement in the best musical–comedy tradition and Wally, approximately as grief-stricken as if a caraway seed had lodged in his teeth, exits nonchalantly to pursue his destiny. The temptation to emulate him pierced me like a knife. I half rose from my chair; then, detecting the projectionist's baleful eye fixed on me through the peephole of his booth, I twisted my features into a sickly placatory grin and sank back, resigned to perishing like a rat in a trap.

In the ensuing reel, Harkins, repeatedly bilked in his attempts to flimflam Uncle Enoch out of his pit, cunningly decides to show the old gentleman the fleshpots, and inveigles him to dinner at the cabaret. Junie has meanwhile found herself another dancing partner, though still torchy for the Ragtime Kid. The evening the new team is unveiled, Wally bursts in unexpectedly—unexpected by the washroom boy, it would seem, for nobody else exhibits surprise—and, shouldering aside the interloper, struts a duet with Junie to universal acclaim. Uncle Enoch fumbles on his glasses, recognizes his scapegrace nephew, and once again thunders, "You're fired!" By some process of reasoning I was too dense to comprehend, the revelation that he had been nurturing a gigolo determines Uncle Enoch to sell out to Harkins. The two retire to a banquet room to sign the necessary papers; there is the usual zabaione of misgivings, phony legalities, and the fountain pen that runs dry, and inevitably Wally comes bounding in with the cornucopia of orders he has garnered for B-Jones B-Jugs. Uncle Enoch, exuberant, makes him a full partner on the spot, and his competitor, after a token display of pique, proves that he has a heart of gold under his knavish exterior. "We're beaten. It serves us right," he says sheepishly. "All along we've been calling him a dancin' fool and really he's a commercial whiz." The butchery terminates with Wally imprinting a peck on his sweetheart's cheek and declaring, with a brisk insincerity guaranteed to reassure his female fans, "B'gosh, you're going to be my little B'Junie, and b'join the B'Jug family."

You might suppose that a victim of such cinematic mayhem would excite some measure of pity, and that when I reeled out into Fifty-third Street and collided with a pair of elderly dragons laden with Christmas shopping, I would have been accorded a helping hand. On the contrary, both ladies recoiled and gaped at me as though I were aswarm with caterpillars. "Well!" snapped one of them, pursing her lips. "Pickled in the middle of the afternoon, and in a museum, too. I always wondered what went on in there."

I removed my Borsalino and gave her as courteous a

bow as I could muster. "If I told you what went on in there, Medusa," I said, "those dentures would drop out of your head. Did you ever hear of a dancing salesman named Ves Tibble—I mean an office boy called Wallace Reid?" Before I could adumbrate the plot, the two of them turned tail and streaked for Fifth Avenue. I worked over toward Sixth, found myself a cool, dark clinic with a sympathetic interne, and eventually managed to justify their diagnosis. What the hell, you might as well be hung for a sheep as for a lamb.

Next Week at the Prado:
Frankie Goya Plus Monster Cast

It must have been about a quarter to four when I entered Rumpelmayer's the other afternoon, and except for a pair of spurious Hungarians crouched over their *Guglhupfe*, hissing objurgations at Sir Alexander Korda, the place was empty of customers. A headwaitress, all whalebone and basic black, undulated in my direction, executed a crisp sergeant major's flourish toward a table reserved for pariahs, and dismissed me with a venomous glare as I chose another, at dead center. My request for cinnamon toast and tea engendered such dismay that I ordered a *Dobos Torte* I needed like a hole in the duodenum, but I figured that perhaps my friend Federbush might eat it when he arrived. He had always been an incurable pastry addict; I recalled how years before, while we were collaborating on *Mother Carey's Chiclets*, an abortive musical comedy based on a book by Kate Douglas Wiggin, he used to consume éclairs, napoleons, *petits fours*, and strudel by the trayful, and the fact he had proposed Rumpelmayer's for our reunion intimated that he was still on the starch.

Even so, I was unprepared for the moonfaced dumpling who presently spun out of the revolving door enveloped in a billowing balmacaan, a green velours dicer cocked on his head, and bore down on me with outspread arms. The duckbill nose and shoe-button eyes were still Federbush's, but fifteen years of lotus-eating in Hollywood had not made him any more ascetic. To put it conservatively, he had ballooned.

"Lover!" he sang out, enfolding me. "You look younger than springtime—exactly like the day we died in Wilmington! How the hell do you do it?"

"Well—er—you see, my face never changes," I replied evasively, "but there's this portrait of me that ages instead."

"And eventually we build to a dénouement where you stab the picture and are found dead beside it, a loathsome old man," he finished, tossing his coat at the waitress. "It's threadbare, kid. Oscar Wilde lifted it from Goethe, who copped it from Marlowe, who probably got it from the *Upanishads*. Anyway, you certainly don't look your age. If it wasn't for the bald spot, you could pass for a man of fifty-one."

"Gee, thanks," I said, with the sort of boyish twinkle Lon Chaney used to excel at. "You haven't changed either. Listen, what'll you have? I got you some pastry—you always liked it in the old days."

"Ancient history, my boy," he said tragically. "Shades of young men among the *mille-feuilles*. It's strictly fronds and hot water now—no more carbohydrates for me. One French cruller and I'm liable to drop in my tracks." He waved aside the menu the waitress was presenting and ordered two soda crackers and a cup of Ovaltine. Then, his lower lip atremble with nostalgia, he fell to musing over the past. Did I remember Dave's

Blue Room, a delicatessen at the corner of Sixth Avenue and Washington Place along about 1926? "Boy, what groceries," he sighed. "That Dave was the Michelangelo of the sandwich world. I'll never forget the one he called the Dr. Flandina Reducing Special—goose liver, raisins, Swiss cheese, mangoes, poppyseed, and almond paste. Many's the night I'd stop in there on my way home to dinner and eat two of 'em. I was an iron man.

"You still are," I comforted him. "Anyone who's lasted as long as you in Hollywood must have the constitution of a yak."

"No more," he said. "I'm all shot—a bundle of nerves. Sometimes, after a day at the studio, I'm so hypertensed I can barely find my own Mercedes in the parking lot." Then he added thoughtfully, crumbling a saltine, "Yep, everything's different, here and out on the Coast, too. How long since you been in Hollywood?"

"Pretty near three years.

"You wouldn't know the place," said Federbush. "All those torpedoes who used to run the industry are gone; everybody's an aesthete. Nowadays, they only make two kinds of pictures there—encyclopedic Russian novels and biographies of famous artists. Take this *War and Peace* hassle, for instance. It's eighty-six years since Tolstoy published it and nobody once thought of turning it into a flicker. All of a sudden, four different impresarios are rushing it into production—Mike Todd, David Selznick, Metro-Goldwyn-Mayer, and an Italian team, Ponti-De Laurentiis, in association with Paramount. Both Todd and the ginzos claim that Marshal Tito promised them the Yugoslavian Army for their battle sequences, and they'll probably go to court about it. The other day, Stravinsky indignantly denies a statement by the Italians that he's doing their score. The word around Chasen's, however, is that Julie Styne has already written it on the q.t. That'll give you a dim inkling of what's going on."

"But why is everyone filming the same story?" I demanded.

"My argument precisely," said Federbush. "I said to one of those donkeys last week, 'Branch out, for Crisakes,' I said. 'Why don't you make some other Russian masterpiece for a change? A good lively musical of *Dead Souls*, let's say, with Piper Laurie and Tony Curtis.' Well, I was just hollering down a rain barrel. He never even heard of the property."

"The famous painters are my dish of tea, though," I said. "First Rembrandt, then Gauguin, then Toulouse-Lautrec. Now I read in the paper that M-G-M's busy on a life of van Gogh. You know, it isn't going to be easy persuading José Ferrer to slice off an ear."

"Personally, I doubt whether Ferrer's available for the role," said Federbush. "As soon as he's through being Mahatma Gandhi, he's scheduled to play Goya. Don't tell me you haven't heard about *that*." I confessed ignorance and sued for details. "It all started a few weeks back with Joseph L. Mankiewicz," he disclosed. "Right after he announced he was producing a life of Goya in Spain for United Artists. Within twenty-four hours, an Italian outfit named Titanus Films began squawking. According to them, they had planned the same thing for two years and were lining up Ferrer as Goya and Gina Lollobrigida as the Duchess of

Alba. The payoff, though, is that neither Mankiewicz or these jokers know about the third version."

"Which is what?" I asked, confused.

"The one *I've* been working on under cover," he replied, removing a cigar from a small aluminum dirigible. "Keep it dark, but I'm readying a sensational Goya script using these same two mummers. The only difference is in mine Lollobrigida plays Goya and José Ferrer is the Duchess."

"Rather revolutionary casting, isn't that?" I ventured.

"Not necessarily," said Federbush. "Ferrer has impersonated women before. Don't you remember him in *Charley's Aunt?* That was how I got the idea....Why, don't you like it?"

"Oh, sure, sure, I said quickly. "I was merely wondering whether you wouldn't lose—ah—certain romantic overtones by transposing the sex of the characters."

"Don't be obtuse," he returned. "Basically it's still the same story—two people overwhelmed by a reckless tidal wave of passion which snaps its fingers at the petty-bourgeois standards of the time."

"Only the girl happens to be a Spanish court painter and the boy's a duchess," I said reflectively.

"Correct," said Federbush. "After all, how many people in your audience know whether Goya was a man or a woman in the first place?" His face became animated. "The beauty of my setup is that one sizzling situation piles on top of the next. Like when Goya— that is, Lollobrigida—is painting the Duke of Wellington. All of a sudden, the bluff old war dog digs the fact that his limner is a woman—a beautiful, desirable woman—and he makes a pass. As she's struggling and pleading for mercy—"

"Wait a minute," I broke in. "Why does she struggle?"

"For conflict, goddam it," snapped Federbush, "If she didn't, you wouldn't have any picture. Don't interrupt me…So while she's pushing over taborets and refectory tables to stem his advances, we cut to Ferrer in a lavish suite of the ducal palace, all dittied out in a black lace mantilla and surrounded by these scantily clad duennas that are ministering to his wants. Naturally, they never dream the Duchess is a man, which of course opens up a myriad opportunities for good hoke comedy and maybe even a tug at the heartstrings. Anyway, some powerful empathy between the lovers warns Ferrer that his sweetheart Goya is in jeopardy. He hastens to her studio, arriving just as Wellington is rendering apart her smock, and we climax with a battle royal wherein José kayoes the Iron Duke."

"Sounds plausible," I said. "How are you handling the business of the two portraits? I mean the study of her in the nude and the one Goya painted to show her husband."

"That incident, candidly, I had to drop," he admitted candidly. "It didn't fit in with my approach. Between you and me and the Breen office, I don't think the world is thirsting for a shot of José Ferrer naked on a bearskin rug. When he was six months old, yes, but not now."

"Well," I said. "To be honest, I can't quite visualize Lollobrigida as an Old Master, but I suppose all those wars and bullfights and court intrigues Goya was mixed up in offer lots of scope for drama."

"Brother, you can embroider that on a sampler," said Federbush warmly. "One of my most gripping scenes is where she defies the command of Charles IV to use egg tempera on the famous portrait of the royal family. 'Sire,' she says, flinging aside her maulstick and drawing herself up proudly. 'You may swing me from yon gibbet, break me on the wheel, suffer crows to peck out mine eyes, but by my maidenhead, I shall never use egg tempera.' That sequence is pure TNT, if I say so myself. By the way, what *is* egg tempera?"

"Search me," I replied. "But before it gets to celluloid, you'd better do some fast research at the Art Students League."

"Ach, it don't matter," he said carelessly. "It's the sense of the thing I'm after—the clash of wills. What really bothers me is how to end the story. I wanted to have the two of them going away to Tahiti to begin a new life together, but I'm not so sure it's believable."

"No, it seems out of key with the rest of it," I agreed. "Have you hit on a title yet? You mentioned the Iron Duke a second ago. How about *The Tinfoil Duchess*?"

Federbush shook his head. "Uh-uh," he said. "It has to evoke Goya's work somehow—you know what I mean? For the time being, I'm calling it *The Disasters of the Heart*."

"I'll buy that," I said. "Yes sirree, I'll underwrite that." I arose and extended my hand. "Well, Jacques," I said. "I hate to run, but I promised to pick up my wife at a *vernissage* at five, and she ought to be nearly dry by now."

"It's been a treat," said Federbush simply. "I needn't tell you that if you ever come out to the Coast—"

115

"And I needn't tell you that if you ever come East again—" I echoed.

We left it like that, neither of us predicting what might happen. With people like Federbush and me, almost everything is tacit. Or will be from now on. You can lay money on that.

You're My Everything,
Plus City Sales Tax

Do I take it everybody's familiar with a magazine called *Town & Country*? (If I know my luck, it'll turn out that there is no magazine called *Town & Country*, or else that there are five with nearly identical titles—*Town & Poultry*, *Hound & Gentry*, *Grouse & Peltry*, etc.) Anyhow, the one I mean is a fashionable paper costing six bits that chronicles the activities of the quality, and hence doesn't circulate around the Luxor steam baths or most of the other places I do. Several weeks ago, though, while waiting for the lacquer to dry on a new toupee at my wigmaker's, I noticed a copy of the September issue on his credenza and began thumbing through it. Before I could determine what cotillions were upcoming or which supper clubs the Braganzas favored, my attention was impaled on a singular advertisement for Dayton Koolfoam Pillows. In case you're a square like me, who never heard of it, the Dayton Koolfoam isn't just a conventional bolster; in the eyes of its sponsors it's a whole *mystique* almost a philosophical system. "Yes, Dayton Koolfoam is *more* than a pillow...it's a *way* of life," the text announced with marked exaltation, "for its relaxing sleep-ability

117

rejuvenates you for another day. And it's *more* than *foam*, for its patented process gives a unique, velvety 'open-pore' surface that assures ever-changing fresh air." What corralled me specifically, however, was the superimposed color photograph of a patrician young person musing over a note from some impassioned gallant that contained the following bit of meringue: "Betty dear…being away from you makes every day seem like a week, every week like a month. But here's a kiss…tuck it under your Koolfoam and dream of me."

This inveterate disposition of the advertiser to cuddle, to yoke his product to the consumer's emotional life and stability, is, of course, nothing new. Brand Names Foundation, Inc., a fellowship dedicated to making the public label-conscious, has been piping away on the same theme for quite a while now. Its most touching effort, perhaps, was the advertisement a year or so back that showed a family moving into a new home in a strange city, friendless and utterly without roots. Everybody was thoroughly woebegone, but, said the copy, there was no occasion for despair. Close at hand were nationally advertised wares to restore a sense of kinship and continuity—old cronies, I gathered, like the O-Cedar Mop for Mom, the cheerful red tin of Prince Albert for Dad, Kiwi Shoe Polish for Junior, and Mogen David Wines for Sister. And, it might have added, a full selection of dependable roscoes, like the Smith & Wesson, if things got really unendurable.

Granting the fact that Koolfoam has pioneered in cross-pollinating love and commerce, my sole objection to its romantic correspondence is that it tantalizes instead of enlightening; no sooner does it start a provocative hare than it inexplicably abandons the chase. Just what, I wonder, is the status of the lady's pen pal that he speaks so jauntily of her pillow? Most men in the early stages of courtship, at least, haven't the faintest idea whether their sweethearts sleep in Utica or in burlap, and, even after a *modus amandi* is established, rarely quiz them about their preference in pillows. To be sure, she may have thrown hers at him in a hoydenish moment while larking around her *garçonnière*, but nobody with red blood in his veins studies labels at a time like that…I beg pardon?…Oh, I thought you said something. If, on the other hand, the charmer is intended to be a young matron, are we to assume that she and her husband routinely exchange love letters freighted with advertising? The whole thing becomes more cryptic the longer you speculate on it, and since everyone knows that intense speculation can easily unhinge the reason, I'd like to make a proposal. I have here, by a coincidence that those prone to stagger may regard as staggering, a series of letters very similar in content to Koolfoam's, and I think their perusal might reward the peruser. They came out of a desk I acquired at a country auction last weekend, whose previous owner, a bachelor friend of ours, emplaned quite precipitately before the sale for an extended stay in Europe. Ordinarily, I would hesitate to publish the letters because of their intimate flavor, but as he left no forwarding address and has undoubtedly changed his name by now, I consider I'm not violating any confidence. The lady concerned can fend for herself. She seems to have done ably thus far.

SEPTEMBER 8

GUY DARLING,

I suppose you'll think I'm a silly little goose to write this, but I felt I simply *had* to apologize for Eliot's behavior the other evening at dinner. Also, I can't resist any opportunity to use my new Parker 51, which, as you know, takes the drudgery out of correspondence. Did you realize, by the way, that its patented Vacuum-Flo suction barrel, embodying a revolutionary concept in pen styling, guards against seepage? Yes, it's goodbye to ink-stained fingers and annoying blots. The stationery, of course, is Eaton's Wedgwood, obtainable in eleven inviting colors. It's sort of a hallmark with fastidious people like myself, those who appreciate the finer things. Guy, you'd adore their fascinating free booklet, "The Romance of Paper." Why not send for it today?

I'm afraid Eliot made a perfectly horrid impression on you when you arrived, but the poor dear caught cold on his way home from the office and, instead of employing Vicks Inhaler, your doctor's recommendation at the first sign of sniffles, drank practically a fifth of Haig & Haig. That's his very own favorite, and I guess it's the choice of the discriminating everywhere, because it's light without being heavy and just smoky enough so it isn't clear. Well, the old green-eyed monster always comes out in Eliot whenever he's had one too many, and he started grilling me in this relentless fashion about where I'd met you, etc. Fortunately, I know those moods of his; had I spilled the fact that we'd sort of picked each other up in the lobby of the Bellevue-Stratford, he'd have brained you the moment you walked in. So I acted real vague—

classmate-of-my-brother double-talk—and he quieted down pronto. All that glowering of his, and the playful pass he made at you with the carving knife, was just his way of showing off. Speaking of the knife, did you notice our dinner service? It's Corham's Damascene pattern, and the apogee of elegance from a hostess's point of view. Master craftsmen have lavished years of experience on this loveliest of all cutlery.

Are you by any chance free this Thursday? Eliot has to fly out to Cincinnati overnight for some tiresome insurance symposium, and I thought you might like to buzz over and take potluck. Of course, it won't be very exciting, just the two of us, but I'll get one of those divine Hormel hams—and they *are* scrumptious, with their mouth-watering goodness sealed into each tin in gigantic pressure ovens—and afterward we can laze around the fire and talk if we have to. I've been dying for a chance to flaunt my new negligee from Bergdorf Goodman's. It's so sheer that Eliot won't let me wear it when we have company. Still, I don't think it's fair for anyone way out in Cincinnati to impose his whim on people, do you? Let's teach him a lesson.

Affectionately,

BRENDA

SEPTEMBER 17

DEAREST GUY,

I'm sure you'll never forgive me for popping into your secluded bachelor retreat yesterday afternoon without warning, and I do hope you won't think me terribly forward. Needless to say, I wouldn't have dreamed of acting that impulsively except it seemed the only way out of my dilemma. I was so wet and spent after getting lost on those twisty back roads that when I saw your mailbox, I almost sobbed with relief. And when you insisted on bundling me out of my damp things and sharing that hot brandy punch, I could have hugged you. Or did I? It's all a bit fuzzy, but definitely on the enchanted side. Is that your impression?

Incidentally, I love the upstairs part of your lair, the imaginative way you've treated the walls and ceilings— Kem-Tone, isn't it? It gives such a satisfying patina, and contractors no less than homeowners swear by its durability. So washable, too; cobwebs and lint scamper at the flick of a dustcloth. Everything you've done, in fact, is calculated to extract "oh"s and "ah"s, with a single exception. Will you disown me if I make one teeny-weeny criticism, lover? In poking around the kitchen, I noticed your refrigerator needs defrosting. Now, Guy, we both know that false icebox economy spells whopping electric bills, as unbiased surveys conclusively reveal. Don't put off that visit to your Westinghouse dealer's to see his dazzling new line of 1957 models. The most generous trade-in allowance in years now makes it possible in some instances to get not only a factory-fresh unit but a cash dividend of several hundred dollars as well. My, can't you just hear everyone's budget purr?

I'll tell you a secret if you swear not to repeat it: I'm becoming the least bit concerned about Eliot. He flies into the most jealous rages over positively nothing. Last night, for instance, he suddenly rounded on me and demanded where I'd found the Madras sports shirt from Brooks that you loaned me. Darned if he didn't catch me off balance and I almost told him, but some instinct saved me. I said the laundry'd sent it back with his by mistake. He kept staring at it all evening, trying to place it, because of course you'd worn it the night he met you. Isn't that hilarious? I knew it'd amuse you.

A clairvoyant little birdie just whispered something in my ear. He said that next Monday, about two-thirty, I'd be in the bar of the Carverstown Hotel, at one of those rear tables in the dark, looking for mischief. If you happen to be driving through Carverstown around then, it might be fun to see whether he's right. Aren't you dying of curiosity? I am.

Expectantly,

BRENDA

OCTOBER 1

SWEETIE,

I've never known anything so uncanny as our running into each other in Bloomingdale's upholstery section yesterday morning. Of course, I knew you often ran up to New York for the day, but of all the unlikely places to encounter one's neighbors! We didn't get very much shopping accomplished, though, did we? And I saw ever so many tempting things as we were leaving— those stunning nine-by-twelve Gulistans whose rich, glowing designs complement your furniture whatever its period, the new Waring blender that whips up foamy puddings and sauces when unexpected guests drop in, a whole cornucopia of sturdy gadgets to gladden the housewife's heart. Promise me to browse through their kitchenwares the *very* first chance you get.

The *escargots* in your little French restaurant on Fifty-third Street were delectable, and as for their stingers, I don't even recall leaving the place. Where on earth did we progress to afterward? I have a hazy recollection of an automatic elevator and your fussing with a shoelace, and the next I knew, the conductor was shaking me and calling out Flemington Junction. Eliot was fit to be tied when I rolled up in the taxi. Seems he'd left the car for me at the station as we'd agreed at breakfast, but I could barely focus, let alone remember a trivial detail like that. To make matters worse, some busybody—Ailsa Spurgeon, I'll bet, she's always hated me—had called up and reported that she'd spotted us reeling out of the Carverstown Hotel last week. Well, you should have seen the fireworks. All kinds of wild threats about breaking every bone in your body and hiring a private eye and Lord knows what—sheer bluff, naturally, since he hasn't a blessed shred of evidence except the monogrammed belt buckle you left behind the night he was in Cincinnati. I thought of mentioning it to you afterward, but I hate post-mortems, don't you? So dampening.

I may be attending an alumnae luncheon in Philadelphia Wednesday—at least, Eliot's convinced I am, and it seems pointless to disillusion him. Shall we say the theology section of Leary's Bookstore at one? I'll look properly demure to fit the surroundings, but I could turn into a bacchante in the right environment. Here's a kiss...tuck it under your Chemex and heat your coffee on it.

Consumingly,
BRENDA

OCTOBER 6

MY POOR LAMBIE,

No words can convey how *pulverized* I was at the news. I'm absolutely shattered, but obviously I can't rush over to nurse and otherwise console you, because Eliot hasn't stirred out of the house for two whole days and keeps watching me like a lynx. However, I'm slipping this to the handyman, and with luck you'll get it tomorrow.

You must have been petrified when Eliot barged into Leary's out of the blue and began punching you, but you can't say I didn't warn you; he's a fiend when aroused, and tricky as he can be. I'm convinced after putting two and two together that he must have steamed open my last letter—which I see now I should never have given him to mail—and then sent me a phony wire from Mother luring me up to New York. I wouldn't believe he could be so base; it shows you can't trust *anybody*. Did he really blacken both your eyes, as he keeps cackling to me? When the swelling goes down, try brushing the discolored areas with Max Factor's Pan-Cake. You'll be amazed how this smoother, *balmier* makeup irons out crow's-feet and restores tissue tone. Small cuts and nicks, too, yield to its snowflake touch. At better drugstores and beauticians everywhere.

As soon as you're presentable, why don't you drop over here early some afternoon for a cozy little drinkie? Or, if you'd rather, I could wander by your chalet. Don't be apprehensive about Eliot. He has these tantrums from time to time, but they usually blow over. Oceans of love, and, whatever you do, don't forget to claim

Your baggage,
BRENDA

125

Calling All Addlepates

There's nothing so pleasing and nothing so teasing—if I may borrow the first line of a frisky couplet the quotation of whose second would bring the postal watchdogs down on me faster than they descended on Charles Ponzi—as an annual conclave of experts. No matter what their specialty, from hair styling to sheep genetics, the authorities in every field nowadays seem to regard it as obligatory to convene in a sacred grove once a year, divide into as many panels as possible to insure a maximum of obfuscation, enshroud each other in verbal cobwebs, and, finally, issue to the press a conclusion any newspaper reader could have reached without leaving his bathtub. The latest group of savants to check in thus, I learned from the New York *Times* the other morning while wielding my loofah, was the Institute of Traffic Engineers, which met recently in Buffalo. After a powerful lot of chin music, its membership announced that daydreams are a major crash factor on super-highways. Your ordinary motorist never could have figured that out. It takes an expert to go right to the heart of the matter.

Ironically enough, if you read on in the *Times*

account—and the counter-impulse in my case was so overwhelming that I whipped the water to a froth—the party responsible for the daydreaming isn't the driver but these very experts themselves. It was grudgingly conceded by the traffic wizards that in abolishing so-called normal hazards like sharp curves, intersections, traffic signals, and pedestrian and railroad crossings they had substituted the peril of deadly monotony. The meeting was urged to develop some practical method of jostling the autoist from his reveries when danger of collision impends, and a number of brain waves were forthcoming—"jiggle bars," or concrete castings, safety slogans at intervals, serrated highway patterns producing unusual nonrhythmic sounds, and so on. The one that arrested my loofah in midair, though, was "a special band radio broadcasting with package programs devised by trained psychologists to stir the daydreamer out of his lethargy." An adroit solution, you would think, but evidently the experts held otherwise. Speaking for the New Jersey Turnpike, its chief traffic engineer reported that "while special radio programs had merit, the Authority rejected their use because it believed that a two-hour program necessary to hold drivers' attention over the full 118 miles of the route would cost too much."

As a masterpiece of logic, the statement deserves to be chiseled in Wheatena on every overpass the length of the Turnpike. The Authority, if I construe its meaning accurately, has no particular qualms about the millions spent in evolving those dizzying ribbons of cement, but feels that hiring a writer and a couple of actors to keep the public from flying off them would border on the spendthrift. No doubt it envisions luminaries like Tolstoy and Louis Bromfield confecting the programs, and players of the stature of Judith Anderson and Sir Laurence Olivier. I submit, however, that to curb woolgathering on the highway doesn't present any insuperable task and that the job need not be done on a grandiose scale. Handicaps there are, undeniably; the stargazer should be snapped back to reality without overburdening his heart muscles or making him lose permanent control of the vehicle. The program that ideally meets these conditions, to my mind, consists of a series of vignettes involving people whose stability or caprice affects the man at the wheel.

Let's suppose, for the sake of supposing, that an average young couple, Mr. and Mrs. Pedro Gershoy, are New York-bound on an express highway, en route to dinner and the theater. They have left their five-year-old-son, Naushon, with a baby-sitter in whom they repose implicit confidence. Suddenly, as they sit wrapped in blissful anticipation of the evening ahead, the voices of two teen-age girls emanate from the radio band.

FIRST T.-A.: Golly, this is the best bourbon I ever tasted. Don't they lock up their hooch when they go away?

SECOND T.-A.: Sure, but I know where he hides the key. Anyway, I had a duplicate made. I've got keys for everything in this place. Here's one that opens his desk, and that's for the clothes closet—

FIRST T.-A.: Say, I ought to get some for the Muspratts' house—then I could wear her things, too. Who

128

made them for you?

SECOND T.-A.: My boy friend at the garage. You know, the dark, Spanish-looking chap. He learned how in jail.

FIRST T.-A.: He's *cute*. I love the way he rumbas; it reminds me of Desi Arnaz....Hey, not so much! I'll be looping by the time I get home.

SECOND T.-A.: Relax—Ramón'll drive you back. He's coming over in a while, and we'll have a ball.

FIRST T.-A.: Well, all right, but no more of those funny cigarettes for me. The last time you and I— What's *that*?

SECOND T.-A.:I didn't hear anything.

FIRST T.-A.: It was a bump, like somebody falling out of bed.

SECOND T.-A.: Oh, that darn kid again. He generally drops out about this time of night, and always on his head.

FIRST T.-A.: Why don't you feed him the little white pills I give Archie Muspratt?

SECOND T.-A.: I keep forgetting the name. What is it —barcarole or something?

FIRST T.-A.: No, phenobarbital. Strictly terrif. I slip old Arch a few after his folks pull out of the driveway and he's as quiet as a mouse. Just ask that Loomis boy at the drugstore. He'll give you anything you want.

SECOND T.-A.: Listen, I've got an inspiration. Couldn't we phone him to bring some over? He could drive out with Ramón.

FIRST T.-A.: Honey, at times you frighten me. Not only are you good-looking but you're a genius. Where's that phone book?

An interchange like this, I believe, would effectively galvanize most torpid automobilists, especially the parents of five-year-old boys, and alert them to any threat of collision lurking in the area.

Should the driver—still the hypothetical Gershoy, for convenience—resist the stimulus, the pressure intensifies in the next duologue. The speakers here are a couple of individuals who, in a line or two, characterize themselves as an employer and his office manager. After a brief, funereal passage establishing the decline of profits in the preceding quarter, the conversation gets down to brass tacks.

OFFICE MANAGER: Look, J. B., we both know what the answer is. The organization's full of driftwood. Cut and cut deep is what I say.

EMPLOYER: But we've weeded out practically everybody we can.

O.M.: Nonsense. I could name half a dozen deadheads around here who don't pull their weight. That young What's-His-Name, for instance. The one who's usually daydreaming at his desk.

EMPLOYER: Yep, I've had my eye on him for some time. Living way beyond his means, isn't he?

O.M.: A regular Champagne Charlie. Always touring around the roads, going to the theater, the best of everything. Why, he burns up more in gas than you and I earn in a month.

EMPLOYER: Well, that doesn't prove anything. Maybe his wife's got money.

O.M.: Not a dime. I checked up on the q.t. in his

neighborhood. Fourflushers from way back—in hock to everybody. They even owe the obstetrician who delivered their baby five years ago.

EMPLOYER: Um-m-m. Kind of hate to fire a man with a small child.

O.M.: Lay off the "Hearts and Flowers," J. B. In this business, it's dog eat dog.

EMPLOYER: Still, maybe if I talked to him, gave him another chance—

O.M.: Waste of time. There's only one thing worse than an old fogy, chief, and that's a young old fogy. Boot him out.

EMPLOYER: We-ell, you know best. Give him his notice in the morning.

O.M.: Why not tonight?

EMPLOYER: Good grief, Torquemada, have some consideration. It's after hours. You can't call up a man at home and discharge him.

O.M.: He's not at home—he's roaring along a turnpike somewhere. However, if it bothers you, I'll compromise. Let's send out a police call for him.

EMPLOYER: Since you insist, but don't press any charges. I wouldn't want him to get the third degree.

By the time the broadcast reaches this point, whatever castles in Spain Gershoy has been building are certain to have crumbled, and unless he's very phlegmatic indeed, he steers down the nearest exit, gulping to offset the pressure on his eyeballs. The possibility always exists, though, that he may be impervious to ordinary threats, in which case a real depth charge must be exploded. Behind the guarded voices of the man and girl engaged in the next exchange we hear the characteristic sounds of a neighborhood bar—a tinkle of glassware, juke-box music, etc.

MAN: What do you mean, it's sneaky? He sent you the letters, didn't he? He promised to marry you, give you a Cadillac, a mink coat—

GIRL: Oh, yes, but that was back in '47. Now he's got a wife, and a nice home, and a different job. He forgot the whole thing long ago.

MAN: That's the beauty of it, dope. We're just going to refresh his memory a little. As a matter of fact, he'd probably *like* to buy those letters back, to keep them as souvenirs. I'm only acting as your agent.

GIRL: Are—are you sure it isn't illegal?

MAN: There you go again. I told you I used to be a lawyer, didn't I? All right, so I'm not a member of the bar association at present, but he won't raise any technicalities. All you have to do is invite him over to your casa for a drink, for old lang syne. I'll handle the rest.

GIRL: He might not want to see me. Did you think of that?

MAN: Tempt him—make it sound worth while. Put on something clinging, sympathize with his troubles, and then, when he's nicely softened up, I'll drop in for a chat.

GIRL: Now, Vito, no rough stuff. You promised me.

MAN: Sugar, I never used an equalizer in my life. Honey and persuasion is my tonic, and they drink it right down. Well, what do you say?

GIRL: O.K., I'll try him tomorrow at his office. Boy,

he'll certainly be surprised to hear my voice.

MAN: Yes, surprise is an important element in this line of work.

GIRL: Speaking of that, how did you ever happen to get into it?

MAN: It's a rather long story. Shall we have another round?

Before the New Jersey Turnpike authority jumps down my throat with all sorts of objections, I grant that they are numerous and valid. The three samples above, beamed at a specific type of motorist, cannot be expected to deter others in the same situation—preoccupied elderly clergymen, for example, or a sedanful of ornithologists, or a Goanese deck steward hurrying to rejoin his ship. If they want universality, they'll simply have to float another bond issue and hire James Michener. I feel constrained to point out, however, that there is one class of driver, of whom I happen to be the prototype, that the program could never reach, and for a curious reason. There is no legislation in this hemisphere, inexplicably, that forces one to switch on a radio. There is also no legislation compelling one to take a bath with the New York *Times*. I guess I deserve anything that happens to me.

Nasal-Happy Mamma, Don't You Try To Two-Time Me

One day not long ago, idling through the pages of a sophisticated 35-cent monthly while waiting for the barber to give me my sophisticated 65-cent monthly haircut, I was suddenly oppressed by the characteristic shortness of breath, mingled with giddiness and general trepidation, that results whenever one gets too near an advertisement for Tabu. This exotic scent, in case you have been fortunate enough to forget it, is widely publicised as "the 'Forbidden' Perfume", which means, when all the meringue is sluiced away, that it is forbidden to anyone who doesn't have $18.50 for an ounce of it. The language used to describe Tabu is a chutney compounded of Pierre Loti and the Symbolist poets, so fiery that it sets every nerve aquiver, particularly those controlling the process of regurgitation. "Tabu," pants the copywriter, "a sultry, heady, lid-lowering fragrance that has whispered its way around the globe…intriguing as a suppressed book…exciting as a locked door…heady, sultry, confusing…smoulders for weeks on your gowns and furs, becoming more and more tantalising all the while. In fact," he sniggers, leaning forward until his eyes become mere slits in his unattractive face, "until recently, Tabu came secretly from Abroad." This tender confidence appears to me romantic but somewhat unguarded; when I was a debutante, the United States Customs had pronounced views about smuggling contraband in your girdle.

The rhapsodic text of the advertisement, however, is mere frosting for its art work, which I assume is an attempt to crystallise the elusive quality of Tabu. Two citizens in evening dress, engaged in a refined musicale, have apparently experienced a common libidinal drive and fused in a fierce embrace before a piano. The ardour of the pair is well-nigh volcanic. The gentleman's hair cascades down his forehead and he holds a violin at arm's length as though to pulverise it in his fingers; the lady, her wrists trailing the piano keys, is bent backward in an arc recalling the Camel Walk of 1922. It seems a pity that the Tabu people, while they were so busy stirring the senses, could not have provided some slight clue to a glamorous situation. What provoked it? Had a drop of the sultry, lid-lowering essence whispered its way around the young woman's corsage, ultimately driving her cavalier to distraction? Or is the caress itself taboo for some undisclosed reason? In fine, I resent being inflamed by a pack of upstart perfumers. They play the coquette in the taxicab and, once in the foyer, twist out of my grasp with a casual: "Well, call me up soon, won't you, dear boy?"

In an effort to reduce my blood pressure, but always retaining a spirit of stern scientific inquiry, I submit the following a-priori explanation of the circumstances. Anyone interested in the amateur rights of this harlequinade, for production at schools and churches, should have his head examined.

[Scene: A suburban living room on the Main Line. As the curtain rises, Mavis Huntoon, thirty-three and disillusioned, sits at her Bechstein playing a Chopin étude. Robin Huntoon, a stolid, unimaginative man of forty who lives only for hardware, is seated in a Sleepy Hollow chair fondling some screws and hinges. After a moment, Mavis rises restlessly and moves to the French windows at rear.]

MAVIS (*wistfully*): It's raining again.

ROBIN: Forty-five thousand, three hundred and eleven …forty-five thousand, three hundred and twelve…

MAVIS: What are you doing?

ROBIN: I'm counting my money. (*With an involuntary shudder of disgust, Mavis picks up a limp-leather volume.*)

MAVIS (*reading*):

O swallow, sister, O fleeting swallow,

My heart in me is a molten ember

And over my head the waves have met.

ROBIN: Hot spit. What's that?

MAVIS (*wearily*): You wouldn't understand. It's Swinburne.

ROBIN: Swinburne? I knew a Nate Swinburne once. He ran a hardware store in Mystic, Connecticut. …Why, what's the matter?

MAVIS (*with a strangled sob*): I can't stand it! I'm stifling here!

ROBIN: It *is* kind of close, now you mention it. I'll open a window.

MAVIS (*coming up close to him*): Robin, don't you notice anything different about me?

ROBIN (*sniffing*): Hm-m-m. Why, yes, you've got a funny smell.

MAVIS: Don't you find me heady, sultry, confusing?

ROBIN: No. (*critically*) But you've put on a lot of weight lately.

MAVIS: Have I?

ROBIN: You certainly have. You're as big as a house. And your slip is showing.

MAVIS: I'm not wearing a slip.

ROBIN: Well, it would show if you were.

MAVIS: Anything else?

ROBIN: Maybe I shouldn't call attention to it.

MAVIS: No, no, darling. By all means call attention to it.

ROBIN: You're getting wrinkles under the eyes. And a scraggly neck, like a turkey.

MAVIS: Not much gets past you, does it?

ROBIN (*comfortably*): I guess I'm just about as wide awake as anybody in the hardware business.

MAVIS: Well, look again. You've missed something.

ROBIN (*starting*): Why, you're holding a little gun.

MAVIS: Aha. And now I pull back this gadget on top.

ROBIN: What are you doing that for?

MAVIS: We call it "fanning back the hammer". (*She drills Robin neatly between the eyes. As she breaks the breech and thoughtfully extracts the shell, the doorbell sounds. With a moue of distaste, Mavis takes Robin by the necktie and rolls him behind the davenport. Then, applying a hint of Tabu to her lobes, she crosses to the door. Locksley Mendoza enters, wrapped in an Inverness cape. His handsome face is lean, coolly ironic, bronzed by tropical suns. As Mavis moves wordlessly to her Bechstein, Mendoza whips out a priceless Amati from its case and they launch into Jocelyn's "Berceuse". Suddenly a harsh oath escapes his lips; he drops the bow, seizes Mavis in a grip of wool.*)

MENDOZA: *Sapristi!* You turn a man's bones to water inside his skin, you she-devil.

MAVIS (*struggling*): Oh, my very dear, you can't—you mustn't. It is "taboo".

MENDOZA: "Taboo"? When two people are loving each other until the seams are coming apart in the clothes, it is "taboo"?

MAVIS: No, no, it cannot be.

MENDOZA (*hoarsely*): I tell you the blood is boiling in my veins! You are a candy store filled with luscious nougats, a henhouse from which the pullets have yet to be stolen!

MAVIS: Promise me one thing. Whatever happens— whatever they should tell you about me—we'll always have this moment together.

MENDOZA: *Parbleu!* Do you think I am a milk-sap, that you can put me off with your bobbery? What stands between us—this man's foot sticking out from behind the davenport?

MAVIS: Of course not. It's—well—it's that you're not the man I thought you were. Who are you, anyway?

MENDOZA: (*simply*): The exterminator.

MAVIS: Then why the violin?

MENDOZA: Just an attention-getter. Nowadays you got to dramatise yourself. (*Extracting a pasteboard box*) Can I interest you in our new brand of bedbug powder? It's a ripsnorter.

MAVIS (*sadly*): I think not. After all, *mon vieux*, in a sense we're competitors.

MENDOZA: But how?

Nasal-Happy Mamma

Mavis (*gently*): You see, darling, I'm something of an exterminator myself. (*As she produces her heater and fans back the hammer a second time*)

CURTAIN

White Bimbo, Or, Through Dullest Africa With Three Sleepy People

Take one thing with another, there are few places I know better than the heart of Africa. Set me down in Bechuanaland or the Cameroons and I will find my way home with less difficulty than I would from Rittenhouse Square or Boylston Street. My entire youth, in a sense, was spent on the dark Continent. By the time I was eleven, I was probably the world's foremost authority on the works of Sir H. Rider Haggard, or at least the foremost eleven-year-old authority in Providence, Rhode Island. My impersonation of Allan Quatermain tracking down a spoor was so exact and so forthright that a popular movement sprang up among my fellow-citizens to send me to Mombasa. I was, however, not quite ready for Mombasa and begged off. At fifteen, I could quote Livingstone and Paul Du Chaillu so glibly that my sponsors revived their project, this time offering to send me to Tanganyika. It became sort of a good-humoured tug of war to get me out of New England. I don't want to sound chesty, but I suppose I've done more harm to Africa in my day than Cecil Rhodes.

It came as a pang, therefore, to learn that my achievement had been overshadowed by that of a complete unknown, a person whose names occur in no encyclopedia or reference work on Africa. Armand Brigaud may well be a familiar figure in the Explorers' Club, and he can probably be found any afternoon at the National Geographic Society swapping yarns with William Beebe and Burton Holmes. Frankly, I never heard of him until yesterday, when I picked up a yellowing copy of a pulp magazine called *Jungle Stories* and read his novelette, *Killers on Safari*. Though it costs me an effort, I shall give the man his due. In *Killers on Safari*, Armand Brigaud has written finis to the subject of Africa. After him, the deluge. Me, I'll have a double deluge with very little soda, please.

To be quite candid, the safari the author celebrates in his title is about as exciting as a streetcar journey from New Haven to Savin Rock, and his flora and fauna suggests the lobby display accompanying a Monogram jungle film. What lifts *Killers on Safari* from the ruck is a cast of characters out of Daisy Ashford by Fenimore Cooper, with Superman acting as accoucheur. Their adventures are recorded in some of the most stylish prose to flow out of an inkwell since Helen Hunt Jackson's *Ramona*. The people of Mr. Brigaud's piece, beset by hostile aborigines, snakes, and blackwater fever, converse with almost unbearable elegance, rolling out their periods like Edmund Burke. Here, for example, Diana Patten and Walter Huntley, a couple of the characters, in a sylvan glade, as their porters take a short breather:

"A coarse forest pig shuffled out of a ravine and began nibbling on a bamboo root. The shapely hand of

Diana Patten made a gesture which encompassed the whole scene as she said softly: 'These beasts of the wilderness know when it is safe for them to come near the most murderous of all mammals: man!' Walter Huntley stared adoringly at her symmetrical features, which became so girlish and gentle when her red lips parted in a smile. For the thousandth time he thought that she was unusually tall, but breath-takingly gorgeous, from her wavy blonde hair down her statuesque body to her shapely feet. The big pig trotted back into the ravine."

This tropical idyll pauses for approximately twelve hundred words of exposition to establish Diana's and Walter's identity, and then:

"The forest hog emerged again from the ravine, leading a sow and four piglets. 'Are they not coarse, rough, and as perfectly alike as rain-drops in every detail excepting size?' Diana chuckled, snuggling against Walter's shoulder." I cannot recall a more engaging passage in fiction, and I've been trying for almost eighteen seconds.

The principals of *Killers on Safari* are three: Dr. Hargrave, a goatish New York physician travelling through Sierra Leone on a scientific mission vaguely related to rejuvenation; Walter Huntley, his guide, a former patron of alcoholic beverages, seeking salvation; and Diana Patten, the doctor's nurse. Judged by ordinary hospital standards, Diana is the least conventional nurse ever sent out by a registry. The decorative heading represents her as a toothsome showgirl, clad in a minute swatch of rayon and transfixing a gigantic black warrior with an assagai. "As a student in a women's college, she had won prizes in archery and javelin-throwing contests," Mr. Brigaud fluently explains. Diana, in all justice, has her softer side; somewhat later, when she and Walter are rushed by a savage, she cries out instinctively: "Don't kill him, but put a bullet into one of his legs!" Diana's innate sentimentality continually gets in her way; further on, a black chieftain named Wambogo invites her to share his pallet and she taunts him into duelling with javelins, with this result: "It would have been easy for her to disembowel Wambogo before the latter could bring his own spear into play. But she preferred to maim him....Therefore she split open Wambogo's breast muscles, and cut his tendons under his armpit. Then, as he howled with pain and rage, she slid out of his grasp, leaped back, and pinked him through a leg." Lucky for Wambogo that Diana was only pettish, as she might really have unsheathed her claws.

The story opens with Diana warning Walter that their employer, Dr. Hargrave, has become jealous of their attachment and means him no good. Her apprehensions are justified, for the Doctor is ever-lastingly crouched in the shrubbery, tremulous with desire, cooking up schemes for eliminating the guide. At length he eggs on a treacherous native named Itira Nlembi to ambush Walter, but the latter draws first claret and the aggressor slinks off into the potted palms with the equivalent of a broken neck. The party now proceeds sluggishly to the territory of a tribe of fierce hallboys called the Amutu, where Dr. Hargrave divides his time between healing the sick and pinching Diana. She finds his attentions odious and haughtily terms him a boor. Dr. Hargrave smarts under the insult:

" 'So I am called a boor!' he mouthed angrily. 'I begin to have enough of your sponsoring the cause of the former tramp, Miss Patten!' And turning on his heels, he strode furiously toward the central pavilion....When the portly bulk of Hargrave disappeared behind the lap [*sic*] of the pavilion acting as a door, her spirits sank and she moaned: 'From bad to worse! It is bad, very bad, to be under orders of a man on the verge of insanity! I wonder how it will all end!' " It all ends quite spiritedly, with Hargrave putting a slug in the guide's ribs and Walter bringing his revolver butt down on the Doctor's skull. This surprisingly restores good-fellowship all around, and the rivals unite to repulse an attack by the Amutu. Hargrave herewith exits untidily from the plot, struck down by a battle axe, but thanks to a homemade avalanche and some fast spear work by Diana, Walter and the girl get clear. It then transpires how foresighted Diana was to major in archery at college; she keeps the larder well stocked with antelope meat and liquidates a black leopard who waylays her in the greenery. Some index of her pluck on this occasion may be gained from Walter's words following the event:

" 'You acted with amazing spunk and skill. You are a marvellous heroine. But, damn it! For a moment I nearly got a stroke at the thought that that awful lion was about to tear you to shreds!' " He implores Diana not to go hunting unescorted in future, but, womanlike, she disregards him and sallies forth. Thereupon her lover behaves much in the manner of a Keystone two-reeler: "Walter tore his hat from his head, slammed it on the ground, and kicked it." Whether he jumped up and down on it or flung a custard pie after her is not in-dicated. His blood pressure again starts vaulting when a courier reports that Diana has been taken captive by Itira Nlembi: "Walter saw blood on his face, and on one of his arms, and almost got a stroke." Walter, in fact, constantly appears to be hovering on the edge of a syncope; the next time he sees Diana, in Itira's lair, he reacts characteristically: "Walter nearly became apoplectic at the sight of her dishevelled hair, bruised arms, and torn clothes." My knowledge of hypertension is elementary, but it seems to me Walter would be far better off rocking on the porch of a New Jersey milk farm than mousing around Sierra Leone.

The story (for want of a better term) now develops what is unquestionably the tiniest crescendo in the annals of modern typesetting. Itira Nlembi, overcome by Diana's charms, offers to make her his queen. Diana responds in her usual polished forensic style: " 'I have been waiting for some hare-brained proposals ever since your evil-smelling grub-eaters ambushed and overcame me by sheer strength of numbers!' " Never-theless, playing for time, she pretends to accede on condition that he court her for two months, as befits a lady of rank. Itira, anxious not to breach the rules of etiquette, assents. Then, aided by two ladies of the harem, the lovers vamoose and race to meet a British relief column they have magically notified. Itira's hatchetmen, of course, give pursuit. At the couple's darkest hour, just as Walter's arteries are snapping like pipestems, comes deliverance: "Walter's calm voice was belied by the feverish look of his eyes and his twitching lips. Suddenly he beamed ecstatically and shouted at the top of his lungs: 'Oh, my dear, there will be no reason of hurting that pretty head of yours! Look down there, toward the north! Don't you see gun barrels gleaming under the sun? They are coming, the British!'" A few rounds of grape disperse the blacks, and the British officer in command benignly advises Walter and Diana to get themselves to the nearest chaplain. "'And,' he adds, with a gruff chuckle, 'could I be best man? I sort of think it would round up my memories of this chapter of adventures spiced by human interest.'"

And so, as apoplexy and archery join lips under the giant clichés and Kipling spins in his grave like a lathe, let us bid adieu to Armaud Brigaud, a great kid and a great story teller. See you around Lake Chad, old boy, and don't take any wooden rhetoric.

Whose Lady Nicotine?

At approximately four o'clock yesterday afternoon, the present troubadour, a one-story taxpayer in a wrinkled alpaca jacket and a repossessed Panama, was gaping into the window of Alfred Buntwell Inc., the celebrated tobacconist in Radio City. Above his balding, gargoyle head floated a feathery cloud containing a Mazda bulb labelled "Idea!" Buntwell is a name revered by pipe smokers everywhere; his briars have probably penetrated farther into the earth's far places than the Union Jack. From the steaming jungles of the Gran Chaco to the snows of Kanchanjanga, from the Hook of Holland to the Great Barrier Reef, the white dot on the Buntwell pipe stem is the sign of the sahib. Deep in equatorial Africa, surrounded by head-hunters, Mungo Park clenched a Buntwell pipe between his teeth to maintain his fortitude; it was a battered Buntwell mouthpiece that yielded up the fate of the Franklin polar expedition.

Peering into the shop, jostled by crisp, well-fed executives hurrying toward million-dollar deals, it suddenly struck me that a Buntwell pipe was the key to my future. Here at last was a magic talisman that would transform me from a wormy, chopfallen cipher into a

147

forceful, grim-lipped tycoon. A wave of exultation swept over me; I saw myself in the club car of the Twentieth Century Limited puffing a silver-mounted Buntwell and merging directorates with a careless nod. I too could become one of those enviable types who lounged against knotty-pine interiors in four-colour advertisements, smoking their Buntwells and fiercely demanding Old Peg-leg Whisky. "Give me Old Peg-leg's satin smoothness every time," I would growl. "I like a *blended* rye."

I squared my tiny shoulders and, baring my teeth in the half-snarl befitting a major industrialist, entered the shrine. To my chagrin, no obsequious lackey sprang forward to measure my features for the correct model. A cathedral hush enveloped the shop, which had the restrained elegance of a Park Avenue jeweller's. At a chaste showcase displaying a box of panatelas marked down to a thousand dollars, a glacial salesman was attending a fierce old party with white cavalry mustaches redolent of Napoleon brandy. In the background, another was languidly demonstrating a cigarette lighter to a dowager weighed down under several pounds of diamonds. I coughed apologetically and gave the salesman a winning smile to indicate that I knew my place. The old grenadier scowled at me from under beetling brows. "Confound it, sir," he roared, "you're not at a cock fight! Blasted place is gettin' noisier than the durbar!" I cleared my throat, in which a fish bone had mysteriously lodged, and made myself as inconspicuous as possible. The salesman hastily explained that the war had brought an influx of foreigners, but his client refused to be mollified.

"Should have caned the bounder," he sputtered. "Country's goin' to the demnition bow-wows, dash it all! Now then, Harkrider, what's this infernal nonsense about my Burma cheroots?" He waved aside the salesman's excuse that a convoy had been sunk, commanded that Buntwell himself be summoned.

"But Mr. Buntwell's been dead sixty years, major," Harkrider protested.

"None of your poppycock!" barked the major. "You tell Buntwell to bring 'em around personally by noon tomorrow or I close my account!" He stamped out, his wattles crimson with rage, and I sidled forward timidly. In a few badly chosen words, I indicated that I required a pipe.

"H'm-m-m-," murmured Harkrider grudgingly, surveying my clothes. "Just a moment." He disappeared through a curtain and engaged in a whispered consultation with the manager. I dimly overheard a phrase that sounded like "butter-snipe"; the two were obviously discussing their lunch. At length the salesman re-entered and conducted me sullenly to a showcase. After some deliberation, he extracted what appeared to be an old sycamore root fitted with a steel flange that covered the bowl.

"Know anything about pipes?" he inquired patronisingly.

"Well, not exactly," I hesitated. "I had a corncob when I was a little boy—"

"I'm not interested in reminiscences of your youth," he snapped. "Hold still." With a quick gesture, he jammed the root into my mouth and backed off, studying my face critically.

"Wh-what is it for?" I stammered.

"Big-game hunting," he returned loftily. I was screwing up my courage to inquire out of which end the bullet came when he suddenly plucked it from my teeth. "No, I don't care for you in that. Let's see now— what's your club?"

"Why—er—uh—the Williams After-Shave Club," I replied politely. "You know, for men whose skins welcome that zestful, bracing tang—

"No, no," he broke in irritably. "Where do you keep your yacht?" His face darkened and he took a threatening step forward. "You have a yacht haven't you?"

"Oh-why—er—bub—certainly," I lied skilfully. "He's—I mean, she's laid up right now, the man's scraping her chimney. It got full of seaweeds."

Harkrider glared at me suspiciously, clearly unconvinced.

"Yo heave ho, blow the man down," I hummed nonchalantly, executing a few steps of the sailor's hornpipe. "Thar she blows and sparm at that! A double ration of plum duff for all hands, matey !" The stratagem was successful; with a baffled grunt, Harkrider produced a green velvet jewel case and exhibited a small, charred stub encrusted with salt.

"That's been used before, hasn't it?" I faltered.

"Of course it's been used," he grated. "You don't think you're going to get a new pipe for sixty-seven dollars, do you?"

"Oh, no, naturally," I agreed. "Tell you the truth, I had in mind something a bit smaller."

"Smaller?" snorted Harkrider. "You ought to have a calabash to go with that jaw of yours!"

"That's what I was telling the wife only this morning," I chuckled. "Gee, did you ever see anything like it? It's worse than an English bulldog's."

"Well, do you want a calabash or not?" he interrupted. "They're twenty dollars—though I guess you don't see that much money in a year, do you?" Blushing like a lovely long-stemmed American Beauty rose, I explained that I merely wanted something to knock around in, a homely old jimmy pipe I could suck on while dispensing salty aphorisms like Velvet Joe. After a heartrending plea, he finally consented to part with a factory second for thirteen dollars, equipped with an ingenious aluminum coil which conveyed the nicotine juice directly into the throat before it lost its potency. To prove my gratitude, I immediately bought a tobacco jar in the shape of a human skull, two pounds of Buntwell's Special Blend of chopped amethysts and attar of roses, and a cunning all-purpose reamer equally useful for removing carbon from a pipe or barnacles from a boat. Peeling eighty-three rugs from my skinny little roll, I caught up my purchases and coursed homeward whistling gems from The Bartered Bride. Right after dinner, I disposed myself in my favourite easy chair, lit a cheery blaze in the pipe and picked up the evening paper.

When I regained consciousness, there was a smell in the apartment like a Hindu suttee, and an angel in starched denim was taking my pulse and what remained of my roll. If I go on improving at this rate, she's promised I can get up tomorrow. That means I can go out Wednesday and go to jail on Thursday, because in the meantime I've got a date to heave a brick through a plate-glass window in Radio City. See you in Alcatraz, bud.

Hit Him Again, He's Sober

Had the late Henry James been standing on the steps of his house at 21 Wellington Place early this morning, he would have seen the deponent, his neighbour, totter out of a cab and collapse with a sob in the arms of the night elevator man. No doubt Mr. James, who oddly enough *was* standing there gassing with Mark Twain and Richard Harding Davis, imagined he was seeing just another drunk. That is Mr. James's privilege; personally, I do not give a fig for his good opinion of me. But I do most definitely want to clarify the incident before it becomes distorted. It is typical of our sick civilisation that a man as temperate as myself, abstemious to the point of fanaticism, should become the butt of gossip. And yet, paradoxically, it was my very sobriety that brought down on me vilification and physical abuse worse than was ever heaped on an early Christian martyr.

The whole wretched affair began yesterday afternoon. When the late sunlight filtered through the blinds on to my Tyrian-purple couch, it revealed a very sick man. Three Lilliputians in doublet and hose, armed with nutpicks and oyster forks, were enfilading my big toe, from which the letters "O–U–C–H" zigzagged away into infinity. During the night, parties unknown had removed my corneas, varnished and replaced them, and fitted me with a curious steel helmet, several sizes too small. Lying there cradled between softest Fruit of the Loom, a deep cocoa-flavoured sense of remorse welled upward from the knees and constricted my heart.

"You mucker," I said through my teeth, "if you've an ounce of manhood in your make-up, you'll get down on all fours and beg her forgiveness." This gaudy monologue continued uninterrupted through my ablutions, except when the can of tooth powder slipped from my fingers and exploded on the floor with a roar like a fragmentation bomb. A few seconds later, I entered my wife's presence with the smug exaltation of a character out of a Hall Caine novel, clothed in a white dimity frock and a blue hair ribbon, fingering the temperance badge pinned to my breast.

"I'm through," I declaimed. "Never again. Goodbye, John Barleycorn, hello, Walker-Gordon. *Mens sana in corpore sano*. Look at this hand—steady as a rock." My peach blossom looked up from her buhl writing cabinet, shrugged coldly, and resumed adding up the liquor bill. Determined to prove I had undergone a moral regeneration worthy of *Pilgrim's Progress*, I conjured up a corn popper and a volume of Colley Cibber's memoirs and snuggled down before the hearth. After I had read in silence for twenty seconds, the pica type tired my eyes and I leaned my head on my hand for support. Suddenly the phone shrilled and I arose, adroitly demolishing a vase of chrysanthemums. Two members of our young married set were holding an impromptu cocktail party. Next to Mrs. George Washington Kavanaugh, they assured me, my presence would establish it as the social event of the season. I was refusing politely but firmly when I heard my wife whinny over my shoulder.

"A party! A party!" she bleated. "You never take me to a party! I want to go to the party! Party... party...party..." Before I could reason with her, she flung herself on the counterpane and started sobbing into the bolster. Aware of the futility of trying to combat tears with logic, I acceded wearily. On the way uptown in the taxi, however, I made it plain that my decision to abstain from alcohol was irrevocable. My wife's lip curled superciliously. "Tell it to Sweeney," she advised. I leaned over to Sweeney, who was beating an impatient tattoo on the steering wheel while waiting for the lights to change, and told him my decision to abstain was irrevocable. His contemptuous chuckle infuriated me, and I lost my head. "You wait, the two of you!" I screamed, hammering my tiny fists on the jump seat. "May I fall down dead if I so much as touch a drop!" I was still defying the lightning as we swept into the pleasure pavilion. Eighteen or twenty voluptuaries, in varying stages of repair, were holding wassail in a cosy two-room apartment. To make the proceedings more intimate, someone had introduced a Great Dane, a parakeet, and a progressive child who was busily emptying fruit rinds and cigarette ends into the men's hats. Yet amid the sickening debauch, suggesting Babylon at its most dissolute (Babylon, Long Island, that is), I stood a figure apart, a pillar unmoved by the blandishments and mockery of my fellows.

"Just one teentsy-weentsy sip," begged my hostess, a tantalising blonde, all black georgette and open-mesh stockings. "Don't be thataway, you inflexible boy." For a moment her dear nearness maddened me, but I resolutely averted my face and called for a glass of Adam's ale. The more turbulent the carousal, the more steadfast I became; Cromwell at his flintiest was an orchid compared to me. In my foolish pride, I believed that I had found the philosopher's stone, that I was immune from disaster. And then the Moving Finger moved. The host, a broth of a boy who had once run seventy-nine yards down the Bowl with the Harvard back-field clinging to his waist, linked arms with me.

"Going get you sandwich," he proposed indistinctly. "Come on kitchen." I rashly extricated myself and stepped away. As I did, he reached down to the vicinity of his tibia and came up with a haymaker that caught me flush on the button. An interesting display of Catherine wheels, Very lights, and star shells flashed before me, and uttering a taut "Mamma", I melted into the parquet. I awoke on a pile of krimmer coats in the bedroom to discover my wife applying a cold poultice to the sub-maxilliary region. In between embrocations, the Angel of the Crimea, her cheeks aflame with Martinis, informed me that I had forever alienated us from the beau monde. I had deliberately pinched the hostess, kicked two Whitneys in the shin, and smashed a priceless collection of Royal Worcester china. I protested I was innocent, a victim of some hideous conspiracy. "I'm as sober as you are!" I pleaded. "Soberer! I haven't had a dram since yesterday!" "Yes, yes," she agreed soothingly. "Help me with him, will you, Ariadne? His legs get rubbery at this stage." Before I could wrench free, kind hands thrust me into a topcoat, jammed an alien derby over my ears in the classic manner of Ben Welch, and hustled me downstairs in a freight elevator. While I kept trying to raise my head, which hung dahlia-like on its stalk, the rescuers started wrangling over my future.

"Take him home...No, he'll cut himself....Who is he?...I know a spot where we can get him some soup.... Yeah, soup's good." I gurgled a feeble remonstrance that passed unnoticed; when the dust blew away, I was propped up at a table in a sleazy bar off the Gay White Way, staring wanly into a bowl of buttermilk. My wife and her grouping had disappeared and a noisy Syrian, representing himself as the owner of a chain of shoe stores in Hartford, was offering to take me into partnership. Midway in his harangue, he broke off and, hailing the bartender as "Four Eyes", ordered him to serve me a highball. The gibe evidently climaxed a long hard day for the bartender. With a hoarse bellow, he hurdled the beerpulls and uncorked a left hook that I intercepted nimbly with my ear. The Syrian thereupon lashed out handily and in a moment I was bobbing between them like a cork. The estimate is, of course, unofficial, but sports writers have since estimated that I stopped more punches than Jaboc "Soldier" Bartfield in his entire career.

I came to in an alley with two handsome shiners suitable for framing and the Hall Johnson Choir singing *Stabat Mater* inside my head. My wife had mysteriously reappeared and, aided by a shrill young couple, whose dialogue had been written for them by Clyde Fitch, was sponging me off. "Now take it easy, will you?" she implored, brushing back my widow's peak. "Everything is going to be all right. Just relax." I closed my eyes with a grateful sigh. When I opened them again, I was lying on a banquette in a clip joint off Amsterdam Avenue. Dawn was peeping in at the window and a spurious gipsy violinist was rendering gems from *The Bohemian Girl*. At the next table, a gaunt trio resembling Picasso's *The Absinthe Drinker*, dimly identifiable as my wife and the Fitches, was sobbing brokenly for Alt Wien. I stumbled to my feet, flung my last bit of collateral at the management, and, herding the revellers before me, started toward the door. Right outside it stood two monumental Texans fourteen feet high, with snow on their hair, clamouring for admission. The ensuing action is somewhat hazy, but as I reconstruct it, our Mr. Fitch curtly bade Gog and Magog step aside, employing the informal phrase "you big crackers". I was scudding across the sidewalk, primly keeping my nose clean and my lips buttoned, when I abruptly felt myself seized by the collar and hoisted four feet into the air.

"What did you call me, you little measle?" one of the ogres was rumbling. "Why, I'll flatten that bugle—" He drew back a fist no larger than a peanut-fed ham; the breeze from the gesture alone dizzied me. I croaked out a pitiable denial and he let me drop. The fall nearly broke my ankles. In that instant, as I slunk after my party, I reached the most vital decision of my life. Three times in one evening I had pursed my lips against the grape and thrice my life had hung in the balance. Come hell or high water, famine, flood, or fire, I was through with milk and large moral resolutions. From here on, it's high carnival and strange purple sins. Bring me another pair of those amber witches, waiter, and go easy on the club soda.

Why Boys Leave Home

Every woman worth her salt, and even the few unsalted ones I have known, cherishes somewhere in her heart midway between the auricle and the ventricle a lovely, pastel-tinted dream. Maid or matron, she longs to dress up her man in a velvet smoking jacket and red morocco slippers, plant him in his favourite easy chair with a pipe and a rattling good detective story, and then, the moment his eyes freeze over, launch into a catalogue of bargains available at the stores. My own chocolate drop is no exception. One evening a while ago, I tottered in from a gruelling afternoon at the bookmaker's and collapsed heavily in my Morris chair. I barely had time to sluice my larynx with a healing emollient of honey, orange bitters and a drop of cognac to allay the insupportable sweetness before the nightly overture struck up.

"Well, I vum," began my helpmate, unfolding her newspaper. "Do you remember those cunning little doilies Sandra Vermifuge bought two years ago at Neimann & Marcus, in Dallas? She paid a dollar forty-nine for them, and here they are at McCreery's for only a dollar forty-three. I can't wait to see her face!"

"Neither can I," I giggled. "Let's call her up and

tease her! Where does she live now?"

"In Spokane, I think," said my wife doubtfully. "But you don't really intend—"

"Why not?" I urged. "Oh, come on, it's only a twenty-three-dollar toll call!" My proposal was received with an icy silence that melted forty-five seconds later, just as I had relaxed my neck muscles and begun a realistic imitation of a transcontinental truck puffing up a grade.

"Macy's is holding its annual clearance of barbecue aprons," the Voice resumed. "We've got four, but I don't think you can have too many barbecue aprons, do you?…And look at this: there's a sacrifice of poplin-covered steamer chairs at Altman's, eighty-nine dollars and ninety-eight cents, only twenty-two to a customer.…Genuine quilted-rayon cheese strainers, marked down to four fifty-four.…Now here's something we really need!…Are you awake?"

"Urg", I replied, to indicate I was drinking in every word.

"GIMBEL'S JACKS UP YOUR CAR!" she read breathlessly. "GIMBEL'S COVERS UP YOUR CAR. If you're going into the service or to Florida, leave your car protected, so it will stay spick-and-span until you return. Jack it up on our plywood jacks—they'll hold an eight-ton truck for the duration. Then cover it from stem to stern with our paper coverall to keep out dust, soot, grit and grime; it's sturdy kraft paper—"

"Listen !" I roared. "I like the car the way it is! I like it down there in the country with mushrooms in the clutch and chickens roosting in the glove compartment! And if you think I'm going to travel sixty-four miles in the dead of winter to dress up a '37 Plymouth in a paper tent, you can jolly well—"

"Of course not, gingerbread boy," agreed Circe soothingly, "but it can't hurt if I stop in tomorrow and look at it, can it?"

Which may explain how I came to reel into the railroad station at Frogtown, New Jersey, yesterday morning in a sub-arctic dawn, my spectacles opaque with steam and my pigmy frame bent double under a massive carton. The freight agent squirted tobacco juice over my shoes in welcome.

"Back for the summer, eh?" he inquired. "Say, you certainly look awful. What are those big circles under your eyes?"

"Glasses," I said evenly. "What the hell do you think they are?"

"You never got 'em drinkin' milk," he guffawed, slapping his thigh. "Say, what's in that there box?"

"A body," I snapped. "The body of a freight agent with a long nose that he kept sticking into other people's business." There was a short, pregnant silence during which our eyes stood toe-to-toe and slugged it out. Then, humming a nonchalant air, I sauntered into a snowdrift outside and dawdled a scant hour and a half wondering how to cover the seven miles to my duchy without a car. At last a friendly chicken farmer drew up, attracted by my humorous carrot nose, stovepipe hat and lumps of coal simulating buttons.

"Ain't no room up front here," he said hospitably, leaning out of the warm, cosy cab of his truck, "but you can ride back there with them pullets."

For the first couple of miles, it was a novel experience

to travel with a boutonnière of Rhode Island Reds pecking at my cravat, but eventually their silly feminine chatter bored me, and averting my face, I drank in great healing lungfuls of the exhaust. With the perfect sense of timing that characterises everything I do, I arranged matters so that my chariot was exactly abreast of the post office as a group of neighbourhood louts emerged.

"Pretty good-sized capon you raised there, Zeb," they complimented my ferryman. "Figger on butcherin' him now or feedin' him through the winter?"

Their good-natured derision was infectious, and averting my face, I drank in great healing lungfuls of the pullets. Soon, however, the spires of my château came into sight and I vaulted nimbly into a puddle, slashing a jagged rent in my overcoat, and trudged up the glare ice to Lacklustre Farm. Time had wrought few changes in the old place; one or two chimneys had fallen down and passing sportsmen had blown out every pane of glass in the windows, but there was nothing amiss that fifty thousand dollars would not cure.

Divesting myself of my coat to insure a spanking case of pneumonia, I gamely caught up the carton and staggered to the barn where the car was housed. Fortunately, there was no need to waste time opening doors, as the wind had obligingly torn them from their tracks. The trip along the dark threshing floor was uneventful, except that I adroitly involved myself in a rope hanging from the beams and conceived the ridiculous notion that someone was trying to garrote me. I emitted a few piercing cries, however, and it shook itself loose. The car itself seemed more streamlined than I remembered it, until I realised that parties unknown had removed the tyres, along with the wheels. I rarely give way to my feelings, but in the irritation of the moment, I gave those axles a kick they will remember for many a day to come. As soon as my foot stopped throbbing, I routed out an old broom and transferred the dust and wheat chaff which had settled down over the body to my own. Then, arms akimbo, I shrewdly laid out my plan of campaign.

The first thing to do, I said to myself, was to get the car up on the wooden jacks. To accomplish this, I would need a stout tyre jack, which must be in the luggage compartment. The key to the luggage compartment, though, was on my bureau sixty-four miles away, where I had prudently left it. Ergo, I must force the lock—child's play to one whose knowledge of mechanics was a household word for ten feet around. I procured a pinch bar from the toolroom, inserted it under the door of the luggage compartment, and heaved my weight downward as outlined in first-year physics.

After picking myself up from the floor, I twisted my handkerchief into a makeshift tourniquet and decided that the wooden jacks would be superfluous anyhow, as the car already stood staunchly on its transmission. The next step hence was to envelop it in the paper coverall. I clawed up the carton and eventually succeeded in setting up the coverall, though several times the wind sweeping through the barn bore me off into the fields like a box kite.

"Now, easy does it," I said cunningly—I had reached the stage where I was addressing myself aloud—and holding the coverall above my head like Paul and Virginia fleeing before the storm, I crept up over the top of the car and dropped it neatly into place. Unluckily, this left me pinned on my stomach in the dark, slowly throttling under sturdy kraft paper; and acting on a sudden obscure impulse, I decided not to linger. I went through the side of the coverall biting, gouging and scratching, and when I hit the lane, I kept on going. The natives are still talking about the meteor covered with chicken feathers that flashed across the Delaware River yesterday afternoon. And the minute he gets his breath back, the meteor's going to do a little talking himself—to Mrs. Meteor.

From far away, I could hear my wife's voice bravely trying to control her anxiety.

"What if he becomes restless, Doctor?"

"Get him a detective story," returned the leech. "Or better still, a nice, soothing picture puzzle—something he can do with his hands."

The Longer The Lip,
The Smoother The Grift

Do young men nowadays still become hopelessly enamoured of married women easily ten years their senior who have mocking, humorous mouths, eyes filled with tender raillery, and indulgent husbands? Back in the twenties, when it was a lot easier for a woman to be ten years my senior than it is now, I was privileged to know one who fitted these specifications and who inflamed me deeply. By the time the lava cooled, I found that the tender raillery in her eyes was actually pseudoblepsis, a form of myopia, and that her husband was somewhat less indulgent than I had supposed. The experience, nevertheless, had a certain salutary effect. It forever dispelled the notion I had cherished from boyhood that a moustache makes you irresistible to the opposite sex.

I grew one that summer in a dogged attempt to bridge the disparity in our ages, modelling it on those worn by the Coldstream Guards I remembered in the pages of *Chatterbox*. It was a dismal tuft—cinnamon-coloured, rather spiky, inclined to droop at the corners in a depressing Mongol fashion. If I resembled anybody, which was questionable, it was Ginger Dick or

Russet in W. W. Jacobs' stories. After carefully grooming and disbudding it for three weeks, I entered the lady's presence in snowy flannels, negligently plucking a round-bellied mandolin. There was no immediate reaction. At length I yawned, flicked an infinitesimal speck of zweiback from my lapel, and inquired lightly: "Notice anything different?" "God, yes," she replied in a strangled voice. "You look like a dentist. A mechanical dentist," she added cruelly, bursting into a shriek of maniacal laughter. I arose, my lip curling as far as the moustache would permit, and, stumbling over a rubber plant, swept out of her life.

I bare this early scar only to prove that my credentials are in order at a moment when moustaches, for some inexplicable reason, suddenly seem to have become especially newsworthy. As influential and responsible a journal as the New York *Post*, for instance, apparently considers them significant enough to merit a poll of opinion. A few days ago it sent its inquiring photographer out to ask five moustached citizens at random: "Is a moustache an advantage or a disadvantage to you in the business world?" Every man interviewed replied without equivocation that a moustache had aided him immeasurably in his career. All concurred that it gave them a "more mature and distinguished appearance" and inspired "confidence". One of them, a stock clerk, stated: "I am 21, and I find that the moustache makes people think I am much older, and they seem to have more confidence in me." Another, a salesman who claimed that he was known to the business world as "Lester with the Moustache", said: "A moustache seems to give the customer confidence that he is dealing with a person who knows his business."

Now, gracious knows I approve wholeheartedly of anything that tends to banish distrust and engender a universal spirit of faith, but I doubt that a few hundred hairs on the upper lip, no matter how silky, can supplant a triple-A rating in Bradstreet. The most reassuring moustaches I ever saw were those worn by automobile salesmen around Hollywood, a notoriously factitious crew. These foxy-nosed brethren all had rich mahogany sun tans, luxuriant moustaches stiff with pomade, and prematurely white wavy hair. Max Beerbohm once observed that men with prematurely white hair are invariably charlatans. The average Hollywood foxy-nose was acutely aware of this (he was, needless to say, a constant reader of Beerbohm), and he sought to offset it by camouflaging himself with a solid, executive moustache. He fooled nobody—nobody, that is, except me.

How the particular one I recall ever tracked me to the dispiriting hacienda where I lay brooding I cannot imagine; it was the least prepossessing in a weedy suburb full of raw-wood addicts, astrologers, and obscure fire worshippers. I found him smirking on the doorstep one dank forenoon as I was reaching for my morning avocado. He wore a rough shooting coat of hyper-tweed and woven wire, a primrose-yellow muffler tied Ascot fashion, brogues that had been perforated until they were simply scraps of leather, and a silver signet ring weighing just under four pounds. The twin points of his moustache were needle-sharp and he exhaled a scent of fabulously expensive cologne.

"Howdy, Aguinaldo," he saluted, clapping me familiarly on the back. "The lady of the house in?"

"I'm the lady of the house," I said coldly, sacrificing accuracy for hauteur. Before I could raise the draw-bridge, he slid past me into the living-room and zipped open his brief-case, his eyes taking rapid inventory of the furnishings.

"Gloomy little hole you've got here," he commented. "What do you do, store roots in it?"

"That's for me to know and you to find out," I parried. He pretended not to have heard my riposte and drew forth a limp leather manual.

"Now, here's the way it figures, Mac," he began. "The best we can do for you on a new Moosup convertible is fourteen hundred skins."

"Hey, wait a minute!" I protested. "I never—"

"Quiet!" he ordered. "I'll do the talking around here. Now, judging from this lay-out"—he looked about critically— "you want to buy the car on time. Suppose you let us have twelve hundred down—"

I interrupted and, mincing no words, made it clear I already owned a car that he could see on his departure, which I hoped was imminent.

"You mean that stem-winder in the driveway?" he sneered. "That's not a car—that's transportation!"

The cheap gibe at my little bluebell stung my cheeks to flame.

"It's good enough for me," I blazed, "and anyway, I'd drive a—a brewery wagon if it got me there!"

"Where?" he asked.

"Where—wherever I was going," I replied weakly.

"Where *are* you going—to a dog fight?" He chuckled. "You certainly have the clothes for it." I suddenly realized I no longer held trump cards and laid my hand authoritatively on his coat collar. He brushed it aside without rancour.

"Look, friend," he purred, "you've got me wrong. Hatcher & Gonsdorf don't sell automobiles—we sell *good will*."

"You do?" I asked, struck by this profound merchandising philosophy.

"Of course," he said. "Do you think I'd sacrifice flesh and blood for a lousy commission? I'd rather have your friendship." His honest emotion shamed me; I saw I had done him a deep injustice.

"That hits me where I live, fellow," I said shyly. We shook hands.

"They don't come any whiter than you, old man," he said, his voice husky. "Now, get your coat. I want to see you behind the wheel of a job I've got outside. Test its fingertip control, self-annealing shock absorbers, and forty-seven big new features. I don't want you to buy it. As a matter of fact, it's not for sale."

It was either the man's hypnotic moustache or some drug like scopolamine he introduced into my coffee; anyway, on the dot of noon I issued dreamily from the Friendly Finance Company with an empty poke in one hand and the title to a new juggernaut in the other. My chest swelled with pride as I paused on the kerb and surveyed its sleek black body edged with glistening chrome-work, its virginal white-wall tyres. Then, settling my cap like Barney Oldfield's, I crawled in and pointed the nose of the machine toward the open road. Motorists and pedestrians alike bit their lips in envy as I streaked past, annihilating time and space with a casual pressure of the foot. At a traffic light I overheard two old ladies in a battered blue sedan discussing me in awed whispers. "That's Luis Escobar, the South American matinée idol," murmured one. "They say he commands upward of ninety thousand reals a picture. A woman isn't safe with a man like that." I lounged back, my eyes heavy-lidded with boredom, and contemplated trips to Baja California, the Everglades, the Gaspé Peninsula. I might even have Buckminster Fuller design me a Dymaxion trailer, embodying certain innovations I had projected for a long time...

Five miles from the Friendly Finance Company, a horrid temblor shook the motor. Some instinctive mechanical bent warned me to pull into the nearest gas station. I had barely drawn up before a mosque-shaped lubritorium when the car emitted a deep, phthisic cough. Almost simultaneously, a Marmon engine of the vintage of 1928, covered with barnacles, dropped out of the hood and lay steaming between the front wheels. Two minutes later, an incredibly handsome young man, whose prematurely white hair proclaimed him a rare mixture of charlatan and chump, crept out of the driver's seat, borrowed a nickel from the attendant, and rode home on the street-car. He's still looking for a certain auto salesman, formerly in the employ of Hatcher & Gonsdorf—chap with a dashing black moustache. As I get the story, he wants to pull it out by the roots.

Call and I Follow,
I Follow!

For the casual visitor in London averse to ostentation and uncushioned by expense account, few hotels offer the advantages of Peacock's, in Clarges Street. Its rates are modest and its service amiable, its cuisine, by and large, free of the viscous sauces that agglutinate the English menu. The clientele, picturesque without being intrusive, consists in the main of dehydrated colonials with saffron faces, bishops in gaiters, and elderly spinsters who still cling to ruching and avian headgear. For me the chief attraction of Peacock's is its proximity to the shops around Piccadilly and St. James's. After a tonic interval of caressing cardigans and chess sets in the Burlington Arcade, pricing wafer-thin diaries at Mudie's, and rubbering at the Golconda of neckwear and sponges, boots and guns, along Jermyn Street, I love to saunter home leisurely through the twilit Green Park, preening myself on my asceticism. By the time I reach the hotel, my frustration is such that I compensate with a Gargantuan tea of watercress sandwiches, rock buns, and pastry that utterly ruins my digestion. It makes for a stimulating afternoon.

One early evening during my last stay there, I

approached the porter's desk brimful of euphoria and bile to discover a whole sheaf of messages awaiting me. The majority, while flattering, were hardly of paramount importance. Hooper's, the renowned coach-builders, had rung up to advise that they could supply a Rolls-Royce sedan-de-ville as per my specifications, with built-in writing desk and poudoir—the exact duplicate of one furnished to His Arabic Highness the Sheik of Kuwait—for £9,250 nett. A firm of hairdressers in Bury Street wished to inform me that its celebrated pomade, by appointment to the Duke of Rotherhithe, King Philip of Greece, and the Coldstream Guards, was available at three guineas the tin. Kittredge & Bolsover, Ltd., of Pall Mall, would be gratified to have me inspect their summer collection of canes, shooting sticks, riding crops, and whips. Should I require anything exotic in the last, they added, their special-order department was at my disposal.

The final message, though, had a distinct note of urgency. A woman I'll cheerfully call Mrs. Elaine Strangeways had phoned twice during the hour, identifying herself as an old friend and entreating me to ring her at Viburnum 3774 upon my return. The name awoke no immediate response, but the supplication, patently, was too crucial to ignore. Some poor soul—willowy, as I envisioned her, with ash-blond hair and violet eyes—was desperately awaiting succor in, as I further visualized it, a negligee of crêpe de Chine. Vacillation, misanthropy in the circumstances was unthinkable. I instantly bolted upstairs to phone or, rather, as it turned out, to get lost in the Kafkalike network of passages surrounding my room. When I ultimately found the door and forced it, I got an unexpected surprise. A strong whiff of curry assailed my nostrils, and I was confronted by a copper-colored brigadier with tufted white eyebrows, straight out of the pages of *Chatterbox*, lacing himself into a corset. A second later, the scent of brimstone replaced that of curry, and I slunk off peppered by some of the most lurid cavalry oaths in my experience.

Slightly unnerved by the contretemps, I was not at concert pitch when I managed to get through to Viburnum 3774, and my voice may have sounded a trifle brusque. Mrs. Strangeways, in contrast, was excessively kittenish, determined, so it seemed, to tax me for my failure to recognize her. "You faithless man," she simpered. "Have you forgotten me so soon? You used to call me your Lily Maid of Astolat."

"I did?" I stammered, vainly racking my brain for a clue. It was a good thirty years since I had used language like that, and even then I had used it with diffidence. "When was that?"

"Why, in 1926," she said in plummiest tones. "Down at that divine little studio of yours on West Tenth Street. Don't you remember Elaine Abercorn, the tawny-haired goddess you were always writing poems to?" I did not recall myself in any bardic role, but her self-description was promising. "There was one you wrote about my eyes I still quote whenever I'm a bit squiffy. It went: 'Let me drown in the deeps of those luminous orbs/Where many a shipwrecked mariner lies—'"

Crimson at the scope of my youthful ardor, I halted her in mid-dactyl. "Well, well—Elaine Abercorn, as I live and breathe!" I exclaimed. "How in the world did you know I was here?" Some movie quidnunc, it appeared, was her informant, and nothing must stand in the way of our instant reunion. "But, of course, my dear," I said, probing warily. "I'd be charmed to meet your—ah—husband sometime—"

"You probably have already," she said frothily. "I've had four since I knew you." The present incumbent, a zoologist at Manchester University, was in Ostend that week, meeting a consignment of Belgian hares or some such jazz, and Elaine was patently avid for companionship. "Do let's have dinner tonight and chat over old times, shall we, lamb?" she begged. "Oh, I've thought about you *so* often over the years!"

I gallantly assured her that she, too, had never ceased to haunt me, and we arranged a rendezvous two hours thence, at a smart sea-food restaurant in Curzon Street. The problem of what to wear gave me pause; ordinarily, I prefer black tie for these sentimental occasions, as a cummerbund flattens the belly, but lacking one at the moment—the cummerbund, not the belly—I compromised on a vest, and flicked a bath towel over my shoes. The bar at Florio's was jammed when I arrived, and I spent a tempestuous half hour buffeted by theatergoers noisily downing triple whiskeys and shellfish. Just as I was dispatching Elaine to the special purgatory reserved for old sweethearts, a giantess in an emerald-green frock trimmed with salmon beads, a veritable grenadier of a woman, wove through the crush and pinioned me. Askew on her head she wore a fawn-colored duvetyn turban whose aigrette was secured by the Hope diamond or its rhinestone equivalent, and from the odor of malt pervading her embrace, I judged that she had fortified herself for our soirée.

"Dear boy, you haven't altered a whit!" she trilled. "Oh, yes, you've lost most of your hair and gained a few stone, but I'd know you anywhere!" She cocked her head archly. "I'm changed, though, aren't I? Go ahead —say it."

"Elaine," I began fervently. "I give you my word of honor—" Luckily, I was saved from perjury by the barman's request for her pleasure—a champagne cocktail, it proved, followed in lightning succession by two more. Elaine apologized; her constitution rebelled at anything but bubbly, and, moreover, she was completely spent from a Homeric day's shopping. Could she recount her purchases? I would be fascinated, I asserted, striking a pose like the physician in Sir Luke Fildes' Victorian masterpiece.

"Well," she said, signaling the barman for a refill, "every time Nevil's abroad, I steal into Fortnum's and buy up all the tidbits he won't permit me. You know, potted shrimps, and Malaga grapes, and honey from Mount Hymettus—that sort of thing. Anyway, today I just went absolutely berserker. I bought three pounds of caviar, and a jar of those luscious Smyrna figs, and some greengage preserve, and a brandied plum pudding—" She leveled a demure glance at me from under her lashes. "You think I'm hopelessly extravagant, don't you?"

"Not at all," I disclaimed. "I'm sure zoologists do very well."

"Nevil?" she said with contempt. "Poor sod, he hasn't a bean—ours was a love match.... Thank you, I will have another, but a touch more brandy. My dear," she breathed, enveloping my hand in her dinosaur paw, "it's angelic seeing you again. I can't wait for you to meet Nevil; he's the handsomest thing. People always mistake him for Rex Harrison." I timidly observed that the same folk were wont to confuse me with Warren William, but Elaine was off on a nostalgic tack of her own. "I'll tell you something weird," she confided. "I met Nevil in this very restaurant, while I was still married to Hilary, my third husband. But what makes it so uncanny, Nevil was corespondent when Hilary divorced me, just as Hilary was named by the man who preceded *him*."

"I—I say, oughtn't we be considering food?" I blurted, overcome by dark premonitions. "We don't have to stay here necessarily—"

"But I want to," she pouted. "I adore this place, though, *entre nous*, darling, Nevil and I never come here any more—they're absolute robbers."

"Then why don't we—ahem—skip dinner, as it were?" I suggested brightly. "You probably aren't hungry anyhow, after noshing on all those sweets at Fortnum's."

My supposition, unhappily, was incorrect; with the emphatic avowal that she was famished, Elaine bore me in to the expectant brigands. Their eyes sparkled and their pencils flew as she proceeded to eviscerate my wallet—pâté, Whitstable oysters, a sole, filet mignon, and a favorite salad of the Nizam of Hyderabad made of shredded five-pound notes. Only cobwebs remained in the wine cellar when she had finished rifling it, and even the sommelier stood awe-stricken. Meanwhile, her effervescence soaring with the intake of champagne, my Lily Maid continued her marital saga.

175

"You never knew my first husband, did you?" she asked. "Benno Vontz, the sculptor—he used to hang around the Jumble Shop and all those bohemian spots you adored. He did that horn-bill in welded steel on top of Neiman-Marcus. A brilliant boy, but terribly erratic, and so jealous—he nearly drove me insane. For six years he kept spying on me and reading my mail everywhere we went—Woodstock, Santa Fe, Redondo Beach, even in Cuernavaca. I didn't have a moment's peace. He'd wake me up in the middle of the day and accuse me of affairs with all kinds of people, like osteopaths, carhops, bakers. I was practically on the verge of a breakdown when I met Ricky."

"What line was he in?" I murmured, making an irrevocable vow to join some Trappist order in the morning.

"He was an auctioneer," said Elaine. "One of those criminally good-looking, virile types—you know, like Dean Martin or Robert Alda. I happened into his place on the boardwalk in Atlantic City, to appraise this ring some woman had given Benno. Well, it proved to be a fake, just carbon, and when I broke down and cried, Ricky bought me a drink to console me. He was so attentive and sweet I just couldn't resist confiding in him, and, of course, one thing led to another. One night, as we were driving home in a downpour, the brakes on his Cord overheated near Arverne and we had to take refuge in a motel. The next thing anybody knew, Benno and this awful private eye were all over us with cameras and flash bulbs. The little skunk had been following me for days; my dear, it was too sordid. Naturally, he named Ricky, along with all those chiropractors and bakers, though he didn't have a smidgen of proof."

Call and I Follow, I Follow!

The realization that I was in the toils of a python far more lethal than any I had ever encountered in Malaya so constricted my throat that speech deserted me. "Wha—what happened then?" I croaked.

"Just what you'd expect," she said, scornfully draining her goblet. "Once the decree was final and we married, I got Ricky's measure *subito*. He was forever mousing around with some popsy, kiting checks and flogging my jewelry until I was frantic. His mother finally crashed through with a few bob so we could come over here. That was when I met Hilary—"

"In this very restaurant, no doubt," I conjectured. Subtly avoiding the pressure of her knee, I moved to extricate myself from our banquette. "Forgive me a second, Elai—" I froze at the sudden expression of terror on her face. "What's the matter?"

"Over there—by the entrance," she said in a low, agitated voice. "Don't look now. It's Nevil. He—he must have got back from Ostend sooner than I thought …Oh, Lord, I can't imagine what he'll do when he finds me here with you."

For my own part, I could, and with blinding clarity. In a flash, I foresaw the whole scene in glorious Technicolor—the confrontation, Elaine's hysteria, the melee as Nevil struck me on the bugle and drew claret, the constabulary's arrival in full fig. Then our visages spread across the *News of the World*, implemented by succulent detail and climaxing in a divorce whose outcome was predetermined: I should have to do the gentlemanly thing and espouse Elaine. The injustice of my plight, so bitter an expiation for an altruistic phone call, hit me like a blow in the solar plexus. As Holmes observed of his death grapple with Professor Moriarty at the Reichenbach Fall, so rapidly does the brain act that I believe I had thought all this out and managed to emit a bleat of self-pity before Elaine tugged my sleeve.

"Wait," she said uncertainly. "I'm not sure it's Nevil after all; I can never tell people apart without my contact lenses. Is he tall and sort of devil-may-care?"

I swiveled about and took a good look at the man. Far from resembling Rex Harrison, he was somewhat under five feet tall, had olive skin and glittering black eyes, and wore an Existentialist beard. While he was definitely serpentine, there was nothing about him either debonair or domestic. I exhaled slowly and arose. The time had come to sever, as delicately as possible, the Cupid's bowknot that had fettered my heart for three decades. Gracefully excusing myself, I slipped out to the coatroom and had a quick tête-à-tête with the attendant —a rather appealing French girl, by the way, with a cameo profile and a willowy figure. Three minutes later, she approached our table with a message from my publisher enjoining me to meet him in Herzegovina at once. I pressed a fistful of notes on Elaine to square the check, kissed her hand in Bosnian free style, and made off down Curzon Street on the double. For the balance of my stay at Peacock's, I emerged only at night and ate exclusively in butteries... Oh, yes, I emerged once by day to dine with a French person I know, but that's another story. And sufficiently droll, not that you could ever tempt me to tell it.

Eine Kleine Mothmusik

WAR ON MOTHS BEGINS

The moths are beginning to eat. Even if the weather seems cool, this is their season for gluttony. Miss Rose Finkel, manager of Keystone Cleaners at 313 West Fifty-seventh Street, urges that these precautions be taken:

All winter clothes should be dry-cleaned, even if no stains are apparent. Moths feast on soiled clothes, and if a garment has been worn several times in the last few months, it should be cleaned.

Clean clothes may be kept in the closet in a plastic bag. It is safer, however, to send all woolens to a dry cleaner to put in cold storage.

Customers should check to make sure that their clothes are really sent to a cold storage and not hung in the back of the store.—*The Times.*

GAY HEAD,
MARTHA'S VINEYARD, MASS.,
JULY 14

Mr. Stanley Merlin,
Busy Bee Cleaners,
161 Macdougal Street,
New York City

DEAR MR. MERLIN:

I heard on the radio this morning before I went for my

179

swim that the heat in New York is catastrophic, but you wouldn't guess it up here. There is a dandy breeze at all times, and the salt-water bathing, as you can imagine, is superlative. Miles of glorious white beach, marvelous breakers, rainbow-colored cliffs—in short, paradise. One feels so rested, so completely purified, that it seems profane to mention anything as sordid as dry cleaning. Still, that's not exactly your problem, is it? I have one that is.

Do you, by chance, remember a tan gabardine suit I sent in to be pressed three or four years ago? It's a very expensive garment, made of that changeable, shimmering material they call solari cloth. The reverse side is a reddish color, like cayenne pepper; during the British occupation of India, as you doubtless know, it was widely used for officers' dress uniforms. Anyway, I'm a trifle concerned lest moths get into the closet where I left it in our apartment. The suit isn't really stained, mind you; there's just a faint smudge of lychee syrup on the right sleeve, about the size of your pinkie, that I got in a Chinese restaurant last winter. (I identify it only to help you expunge it without too much friction. I mean, it's a pretty costly garment, and the nap could be damaged if some boob started rubbing it with pumice or whatever.)

Will you, hence, arrange to have your delivery boy pick up the suit at my flat any time next Thursday morning after nine-fifteen? He'll have to show before ten-twenty, since the maid leaves on the dot and would certainly split a gusset if she had to sit around a hot apartment waiting for a delivery boy. (You know how they are, Mr. Merlin.) Tell the boy to be sure and take the right suit; it's hanging next to one made of covert cloth with diagonal flap pockets, and as the Venetian blinds are drawn, he could easily make a mistake in the dark. Flotilla, the maid, is new, so I think I'd better explain which closet to look in. It's in the hall, on his right when he stands facing the bedroom windows. If he stands facing the other way, naturally it's on his left. The main thing, tell him, is not to get rattled and look in the closet *opposite*, because there may be a gabardine suit in there, without pockets, but that isn't the one I have reference to.

Should Flotilla have gone, the visiting super will admit your boy to the flat if he arrives before eleven; otherwise, he is to press our landlord's bell (Cooper-smith), in the next building, and ask them for the key. They can't very well give it to him, as they're in Amalfi, but they have a Yugoslav woman dusting for them, a highly intelligent person, to whom he can explain the situation. This woman speaks English.

After the suit is dry-cleaned—which, I repeat, is not essential if you'll only brush the stain with a little moist flannel—make certain that it goes into cold storage at once. I read a piece in the newspaper recently that upset me. It quoted a prominent lady in your profession, a Miss Rose Finkel, to the effect that some dry cleaners have been known to hang such orders in the back of their store. You and I have had such a long, cordial relationship, Mr. Merlin, that I realize you'd never do anything so unethical, but I just thought I'd underscore it.

Incidentally, and since I know what the temperature in your shop must be these days, let me pass on a couple of hot-weather tips. Eat lots of curries—the spicier the better—and try to take at least a three-hour siesta in the middle of the day. I learned this trick in India, where Old Sol can be a cruel taskmaster indeed. That's also the place, you'll recall, where solari cloth used to get a big play in officers' dress uniforms. Wears like iron, if you don't abuse it. With every good wish,

Yours sincerely,
S. J. PERELMAN

NEW YORK CITY,
JULY 22

DEAR MR. PEARLMAN:

I got your letter of instructions spelling everything out, and was happy to hear what a glorious vacation you are enjoying in that paradise. I only hope you will be careful to not run any fishhooks in your hand, or step in the undertow, or sunburn your body so badly you lay in the hospital. These troubles I personally don't have. I am a poor man with a wife and family to support, not like some people with stocks and bonds that they can sit in a resort all summer and look down their nose on the rest of humanity. Also my pressing machine was out of commission two days and we are shorthanded. Except for this, everything is peaches and cream.

I sent the boy over like you told me on Thursday. There was no sign of the maid, but for your information he found a note under the door saying she has quit. She says you need a bulldozer, not a servant, and the pay is so small she can do better on relief. Your landlady, by the way, is back from Amalfi, because some of the tenants, she didn't name names, are slow with the rent. She let the boy in the apartment, and while he was finding your red suit she checked over the icebox and the stove, which she claims are very greasy. (I am not criticizing your housekeeping, only reporting what she said.) She also examined the mail in the bureau drawers to see if the post office was forwarding your bills, urgent telegrams, etc.

I don't believe in telling a man his own business. Mine is dry cleaning, yours I don't know what, but you're deceiving yourself about this Indian outfit you gave us. It was one big stain from top to bottom. Maybe you leaned up against the stove or the icebox? (Just kidding.) The plant used every kind of solvent they had on it—benzine, naphtha, turpentine, even lighter fluid—and knocked out the spots, all right, but I warn you beforehand, there are a few brownish rings. The lining was shot to begin with, so that will be no surprise to you; according to the label, you had the suit since 1944. If you want us to replace same, I can supply a first-class, all-satin quarter lining for $91.50, workmanship included. Finally, buttons. Some of my beatnik customers wear the jacket open and don't need them. For a conservative man like yourself, I would advise spending another eight dollars.

As regards your worry about hiding cold-storage articles in the back of my store, I am not now nor have I ever been a chiseler, and I defy you to prove different. Every season like clockwork, I get one crackpot who expects me to be Santa Claus and haul his clothing up to the North Pole or someplace. My motto is live and let live, which it certainly is not this Rose Finkel's to go around destroying people's confidence in their dry cleaner. Who is she, anyway? I had one of these experts working for me already, in 1951, that nearly put me in the hands of the receivers. She told a good customer of ours, an artist who brought in some hand-painted ties to be rainproofed, to save his money and throw them in the Harlem River. To a client that showed her a dinner dress with a smear on the waist, she recommends the woman should go buy a bib. I am surprised that you, a high-school graduate, a man that pretends to be intelligent, would listen to such poison. But in this business you meet all kinds. Regards to the Mrs.

Yours truly,
S. MERLIN

GAY HEAD, MASS.,
JULY 25

DEAR MR. MERLIN:

While I'm altogether sympathetic to your plight and fully aware that your shop's an inferno at the moment— I myself am wearing an imported cashmere sweater as I write—I must say you misinterpreted my letter. My only motive in relaying Miss Stricture's finkels (excuse me, the strictures of Miss Finkel) on the subject of proper cold storage was concern for a favorite garment. I was not accusing you of duplicity, and I refuse to share the opinion, widespread among persons who deal with them frequently, that most dry cleaners are crooks. It is understandably somewhat off-putting to hear that my suit arrived at your establishment in ruinous condition, and, to be devastatingly candid, I wonder whether your boy may not have collided with a soup kitchen in transit. But each of us must answer to his own conscience, Merlin, and I am ready, if less than overjoyed, to regard yours as immaculate.

Answering your question about Miss Finkel's identity, I have never laid eyes on her, needless to say, though reason dictates that if a distinguished newspaper like the *Times* publishes her counsel, she must be an authority. Furthermore, if the practice of withholding clothes from cold storage were uncommon, why would she have broached the subject at all? No, my friend, it is both useless and ungenerous of you to attempt to undermine Miss Finkel. From the way you lashed out at her, I deduce that she touched you on the raw, in a most vulnerable area of our relationship, and that brings me to the core of this communication.

Nowhere in your letter is there any direct assertion that you *did* send my valuable solari suit to storage, or, correlatively, that you are *not* hiding it in the back of the store. I treasure my peace of mind too much to sit up here gnawed by anxiety. I must therefore demand from you a categorical statement by return airmail special delivery. Is this garment in your possession or not? Unless a definite answer is forthcoming within forty-eight hours, I shall be forced to take action.

Yours truly,

S. J. PERELMAN

NEW YORK CITY,
JULY 27

DEAR MR. PERLEMAN:

If all you can do with yourself in a summer place is hang indoors and write me love letters about Rose Finkel, I must say I have pity on you. Rose Finkel, Rose Finkel—why don't you marry this woman that you are so crazy about her. Then she could clean your suits at home and stick them in the icebox—after she cleans that, too. What do you want from me? Sometimes I think I am walking around in a dream.

Look, I will do anything you say. Should I parcel-post the suit to you so you can examine it under a microscope for holes? Should I board up my store, give the help a week free vacation in the mountains, and bring it to you personally in my Cadillac? I tell you once, twice, a million times—it went to cold storage. I didn't send it myself; I gave orders to my assistant, which she has been in my employ eleven years. From her I have no secrets, and you neither. She told me about some of the mail she found in your pants.

It is quite warm here today, but we are keeping busy and don't notice. My tailor collapsed last night with heat prostration, so I am handling alterations, pressing, ticketing, and hiding customers' property in the back of the store. Also looking up psychiatrists in the Yellow Pages.

Yours truly,
S. MERLIN

GAY HEAD, MASS.,
JULY 29

DEAR MR. MERLIN:

My gravest doubts are at last confirmed: You are unable to say unequivocally, without tergiversating, that you *saw* my suit put into cold storage. Knowing full well that the apparel was irreplaceable, now that the British Raj has been supplanted—knowing that it was the keystone of my entire wardrobe, the *sine qua non* of sartorial taste—you deliberately entrusted it to your creature, a cat's-paw who you admit rifles my pockets as a matter of routine. Your airy disavowal of your responsibility, therefore, leaves me with but one alternative. By this same post, I am delegating a close friend of mine, Irving Wiesel, to visit your place of business and ferret out the truth. You can lay your cards on the table with Wiesel or not, as you see fit. When he finishes with you, you will have neither cards nor table.

It would be plainly superfluous, at this crucial stage in our association, to hark back to such petty and characteristic vandalism as your penchant for jabbing pins into my rainwear, pressing buttons halfway through lapels, and the like. If I pass over these details now, however, do not yield to exultation. I shall expatiate at length in the proper surroundings; viz., in court. Wishing you every success in your next vocation,

Yours truly,
S. J. PERELMAN

DEAR MR. PERLMAN:

I hope you received by now from my radiologist the two X-rays; he printed your name with white ink on the ulcer so you should be satisfied that you, and you alone, murdered me. I wanted him to print also "Here lies an honest man that he slaved for years like a dog, schlepped through rain and snow to put bread in his children's mouths, and see what gratitude a customer gave him," but he said there wasn't room. Are you satisfied now, you Cossack you? Even my *radiologist* is on your side.

You didn't need to tell me in advance that Wiesel was a friend of yours; it was stamped all over him the minute he walked in the store. Walked? He was staggering from the highballs you and your bohemian cronies bathe in. No how-do-you-do, explanations, nothing. Ran like a hooligan to the back and turned the whole stock upside down, pulled everything off the racks. I wouldn't mind he wrecked a filing system it cost me hundreds of dollars to install. Before I could grab the man, he makes a bee-line for the dressing room. So put yourself for a second in someone else's shoes. A young, refined matron from Boston, first time in the Village, is waiting for her dress to be spot-cleaned, quietly loafing through *Harper's Bazaar*. Suddenly a roughneck, for all she knows a plain-clothesman, a junkie, tears aside the curtain. Your delegate Wiesel.

I am not going to soil myself by calling you names, you are a sick man and besides on vacation, so will make you a proposition. You owe me for cleaning the suit, the destruction you caused in my racks, medical advice, and general aggravation. I owe you for the suit, which you might as well know is kaput. The cold-storage people called me this morning. It seems like all the brownish rings in the material fell out and they will not assume responsibility for a sieve. This evens up everything between us, and I trust that on your return I will have the privilege of serving you and family as in years past. All work guaranteed, invisible weaving our specialty. Please remember me to your lovely wife.

Sincerely yours,
STANLEY MERLIN

Portrait of the Artist as a Young Mime

"Song Without End" features the highlights of Franz Liszt's life....The music was recorded by Jorge Bolet, one of America's foremost pianists....Most dramatic story behind the scenes of the making of "Song Without End" was the coaching of Dirk Bogarde by Victor Aller to enable the actor to give a flawless visual performance at the keyboard to match Bolet's already recorded score. Mr. Aller, a master pianist, also is Hollywood's best known piano coach for stars. Dirk Bogarde had never played a note in his life! Not only did he have to learn how to play the piano—he had to learn to play like genius Franz Liszt.

—The Journal-American.

The day started off, as all mine do, at a snail's pace. I got to my studio on Carmine Street about a quarter of ten, closed the sky-light and lit the kerosene stove—oxygen, however essential to aeronautics and snorkeling, is death to the creative process—and settled down with the coffee and Danish I pick up every morning en route from the subway. Then I emptied the ashtrays into the hall and washed out a few brushes, meanwhile listening to WQXR and studying the canvas I had on the easel. Shortly before eleven, I ran out of excuses for cerebration and began mixing my colors. That's inevitably the moment some nuisance takes it into his head to phone, and in this case it was the bloodiest of them all—Vetlugin, my dealer. His voice trembled with excitement.

"Did he call you? What did he say?" he asked feverishly. Good old Vetlugin, the Tower of Babble. He opens his mouth and out comes confusion; the man has an absolute genius for muddle. By valiant effort, I finally extracted a modicum of sense from his bumbling. Some Hollywood nabob named Harry Hubris, reputedly a top producer at Twentieth Century-Fox, was clamoring to discuss a matter of utmost urgency. Ever quick to sniff out a kopeck, Vetlugin, in direct violation of orders, had promptly spilled my whereabouts. "I figured it'd save time if he came down to see you personally," he cooed. "The precise nature of what he wants he wouldn't reveal, but I smelled there must be dough in it."

"Listen, you Bessarabian Judas," I groaned. "How many times have I told you never, under any circumstances, to divulge—" Like all arguments with leeches, this one was futile; muttering some claptrap about ingratitude, he hung up and left me biting my own tail. It was a half hour before I calmed down sufficiently to resume work, but I knew the jig was up when the doorbell rang, and one look at the character bounding upstairs confirmed my fears. From his perky velvet dicer to the tips of his English brogues, he was as brash a highbinder as ever scurried out of Sardi's. The saffron polo coat draped impresario-fashion over his shoulders must have cost twelve hundred dollars.

"Say, are you kidding?" he exclaimed, fastidiously

dusting a bit of plaster from his sleeve. "Those terrific abstractions of yours—you don't actually *paint* them here?"

"I do when I'm not interrupted," I said pointedly.

"Well, you're risking your life," he declared. "I've seen fire-traps in my time, boychick, but this ain't for real. If I showed it in a picture, they'd say it was overdone." He stuck out a paw. "Harry Hubris," he said. "I guess you've heard of me."

Other than feigning an attack of scrofula, there was no escape now that Vetlugin had crossed me up, so I motioned him in.

He made a quick, beady inventory of the décor. "Go figure it," he said, with a shrug. "It always kills me an artist should hole up in a fleabag to conceive a masterpiece. Still, everybody to their own ulcer. Zuckmayer, I want you to know I consider you one of the nine foremost painters of our time."

"Indeed," I said. "Who are the other eight?"

"Look, pal, don't get me started or I'm liable to talk all night," he said. "I've got maybe the most important collection in the Los Angeles area—five Jackson Pollocks, three Abe Rattners, two of yours—"

"Which ones?"

"I can't remember offhand," he said irritably. "A houseful of paintings, you wouldn't expect me to recall every title. But let's get down to basics. What would you say if I offered you two thousand bucks for an hour's work?"

"I'd be even more suspicious than I am now, which is plenty."

"A blunt answer," he approved. "Well, here's the

dodge, and you needn't worry, it's strictly legit. Did you perchance read Irving Stonehenge's biography of John Singer Sargent, *The Tortured Bostonian*?"

I shook my head, and he frowned.

"You're the one guy in America that didn't," he said. "In my humble opinion, it's going to make the greatest documentary-type motion picture since *Lust for Life*. Just visualize Rob Roy Fruitwell in the leading role and tell me how it could miss."

I visualized as best I could, but, never having heard of the man, got nowhere. "Who is he?" I asked.

"Rob Roy?" Hubris's scorn for my ignorance was Olympian. "Only the biggest potential draw in pictures today, that's all," he affirmed. "Properly handled, Fruitwell can be another Kirk Douglas, *and*," he went on, lowering his voice, "I'll breathe you something in strictest confidence. After he has his dimple deepened next spring, you won't be able to tell them apart. My immediate headache, though, and the reason I contacted you, is this. The kid's a born actor and he'll play the hell out of Sargent, but thus far he's appeared exclusively in horse operas—Westerns. What he requires is a little coaching from an expert—a professional artist like you."

"My dear Mr. Hubris," I said. "If you think I can transform a numskull into a master in one lesson—"

"For crisakes, smarten up, will you?" he implored. "All you got to furnish is the pantomime. Show him how to hold a brush, what a palette's for, which end of the tube the color comes out. Remember, this lug don't know from beauty or the Muse. Two years ago he was a busboy in Fort Wayne."

"But I've never dealt with actors," I objected. "I haven't the faintest clue to their mentality."

"Mentality's one problem you won't have with Rob Roy Fruitwell, brother," Hubris guaranteed. "He's got none. He's just a matzo ball, a sensitized sponge that'll soak up the info you give him and delineate it on the screen."

"Well, I'd have to think it over," I said. "I'm assembling a show at the moment—"

"So your dealer mentioned," he said. "And believe me, Mr. Zuckmayer, I feel like a rat pressuring you, but the point is, we're in a bind. You see, in view of the fact that we start shooting Friday, I had Rob Roy sky in from the Coast last night solely on purpose to huddle with you."

"Then you can jolly well sky him back," I began, and stopped short. After all, if this gasbag was aching to shell out a fat fee for an hour of *expertise*, it'd be downright loony to stand on dignity; my anemic budget could certainly use a transfusion. Obviously sensing I was tempted, Hubris threw in the clincher. Not only would he raise the ante another five hundred, but he was prepared to hand over a check on the spot provided I saw Fruitwell that afternoon. "Well-l-l, all right," I said, overborne. "Have him down here at four o'clock and I'll see what I can do."

"Attaboy!" chortled my caller, whipping out a pen. "You mark my words, Zuckmayer—this may be a turning point in your career. Once the critics dig your name up there in the credits—'Artistic Consultant to the Producer, Harry Hubris'—the whole industry'll be knocking on your door !"

"Don't bother to freeze my blood, please," I said. "Just write out the check."

Hubris made no pretense of concealing his umbrage. "You're a strange apple," he said. "What makes all you artists so anti-social?"

I knew why, but it would have been too expensive to reply. I needed the money.

I was tied up at the framer's after lunch, discussing a new molding of kelp on tinfoil for my show, and didn't get back to the studio until four-fifteen. There was a big rented Cadillac parked outside, the driver of which, a harassed plug-ugly in uniform, was standing off a mob of teen-agers screeching and waving autograph books. We had a dandy hassle proving I was kosher, but he finally let me upstairs to the unholy trinity awaiting me. Fruitwell was a standard prize bullock with a Brando tonsure and capped teeth, in a gooseneck sweater under his Italian silk suit which kept riding up to expose his thorax. His agent, a fat little party indistinguishable from a tapir, had apparently been summoned from the hunt, for he wore a Tattersall vest and a deep-skirted hacking coat. The third member of the group, a bearded aesthete dressed entirely in suède, flaunted a whistle on a silver chain encircling his throat. "I'm Dory Gallwise, the assistant director," he introduced himself. "We had to force the lock to get in here. Hope you don't mind."

"Not at all," I said. "Sorry the place is such a pigsty, but—well, you know how bohemians are."

"Oh, it's not so bad," he said graciously. "Of course, as I was just explaining to Rob Roy here, the studio he'll occupy as Sargent will be a lot more imposing. The size

195

of Carnegie Hall, in fact."

"*Natürlich*," I said. "Now, before we commence, Mr. Fruitwell, do you have any questions about art? Anything you'd like me to clarify?"

Immersed in contemplation of a torso on the wall, the young man did not respond at once. Then he lifted his head sleepily. "Yeah, this thing here," he said. "What's it supposed to be—a woman?"

I admitted I had embodied certain female elements, and he snickered.

"You really see that when you look at a dame?" he asked, with a quizzical smile. "Bud, you need therapy. Don't he, Monroe?"

His agent shot me a placatory wink. "Well, I wouldn't go *that* far, Rob Roy," he temporized. "Mr. Zuckmayer reacts to the world around him in a particular way—through the intellect, shall we say? He embodies certain elements—"

"Don't give me that bushwa," the other retorted. "I've dated Mamie van Doren, Marilyn Maxwell, and Diana Dors, and take it from me, pappy, they don't have any corners like that. This moke's in trouble."

"Ha, ha—who isn't?" Gallwise put in with wild gaiety. He cleared his throat nervously. "Listen, boys, let's not hold up Mr. Zuckmayer—he's a busy person." Snapping open his dispatch case, he drew forth a smock and a beret. "Here, Rob Roy, slip these on so you'll get used to the feel of 'em."

"Wait a second," said Fruitwell, clouding over, and wheeled on Monroe. "What the hell are we making, a costume picture? You said I wear a sweat shirt and dungarees."

"In the love scenes, baby," Monroe specified, "but when you're sketching, and like dreaming up your different masterpieces, why, they got to blueprint you're an artist. It establishes your identity."

"Sure, the way a sheriff puts on a tin star," said Gallwise.

"Or a busboy his white coat," I added helpfully.

Fruitwell turned and gave me a long, penetrating look. Then, evidently concluding his ears had deceived him, he surlily donned the habit, and for the next quarter of an hour submitted himself to our charade. I soon perceived that Hubris's depiction of him as a chowderhead was rank flattery. Totally devoid of either co-ordination or the ability to retain, he lumbered about upsetting jars of pigment, gashed himself disastrously with my palette knife, and in a burst of almost inspired clumsiness sprayed fixative into Monroe's eyeball, temporarily blinding the poor wretch. While the latter lay prostrate, whimpering under the poultices with which Gallwise and I rushed to allay his torment, Rob Roy leaned out of the skylight to mollify his fans. Since, however, they had dispersed meanwhile, his largess was wasted, and he was in a distinct pet by the time Monroe was ambulatory.

"You guys through playing beatnik?" he fretted. "Come on, let's blow. If the dauber's got any more dope, he can phone it in to Hubris, or I'll get it from research, on the Coast."

"Rob Roy—honey," pleaded Gallwise. "We'll spring you in two shakes, but just co-operate ten minutes more. I want Mr. Zuckmayer to check on a couple of scenes—you know, to make sure you don't pull a booboo. Here," he said, forcibly planting his charge in a chair. "Run through the situation where Vincent Youmans tries to win you back to your wife."

"Hold on," I protested. "How does *he* come into this?"

"A dramatic license we took to justify the score," he said hurriedly. "He's a young music student at Harvard that Sargent befriends. Can you remember the lines, Rob Roy?"

Fruitwell contorted his forehead in a simulation of deep thought.

"Never mind—spitball some dialogue to give the general idea," said Gallwise. "Go ahead, I'll cue you. I'll be Youmans."

"Hello, Youmans," complied Fruitwell, in a monotone. "Where you been, man?"

"Oh, just studying my counterpoint over in Cambridge," said Gallwise. "But you certainly are a storm center these days, John Singer. All Beacon Hill is agog the way you threw up your job as stockbroker and abandoned your family. Can a pair of saucy blue orbs underlie this move, as wagging tongues imply?"

Fruitwell uttered a cynical hoot reminiscent of a puppy yelping for a biscuit. "Women!" he scoffed. "I'm tired of those silly little creatures casting their spell on me. I want to paint—to paint, do you hear? I've got to express what I feel deep down inside me! The agony, the heartbreak!"

His agent, who was following the recital from behind a crumpled handkerchief, sprang forward and embraced him. "Lover, don't change a word, a syllable," he begged. "Do that on camera and I personally—Monroe Sweetmeat—promise you an Academy Award. What about it, Mr. Zuckinayer?" he inquired anxiously. "Does it ring true from the artist's point of view ?"

"Frighteningly," I agreed. "You've caught the very essence of the creative urge. I have only one criticism." Gallwise stiffened expectantly. "Mr. Fruitwell's got his smock on backwards. The audience might conceivably mistake him for a hairdresser."

"How could they, with that dialogue?" he demanded.

"That's what I mean," I said.

"Well, it's a point to watch," ruminated the director. "Remember that, Rob Roy. Now the key scene, where you get your big break from the hotel manager. The plot point here, Mr. Z., is that Sargent's down and out in New York. It's Christmas Day, the landlord's shut off the gas, and he's starving."

"Tell him about the onion," Monroe giggled.

"A bit of comedy relief," Gallwise explained. "He's so hungry that he finally has to eat this still-life of an onion and a herring."

"What, the canvas itself?" I asked.

"No, no—the objects he's painting," he said impatiently. "Anyway, just at his darkest hour, in comes Tuesday Weld, the coatroom girl at the St. Regis that's been secretly in love with him. She's persuaded the manager to let Sargent paint a mural of King Cole for the men's bar."

"Using the pseudonym of Maxfield Parrish," I supplemented.

"God damn it," burst out Fruitwell, "I've got an eight-man team of writers from the New York *Post* waiting to interview me! Let's do the *scene*!"

Gallwise recoiled as if from a blast furnace. "Uh—on

second thought, maybe we don't have to," he stammered, a muscle twitching in his cheek. "I only wanted to corroborate one small detail. Halfway through the action, Mr. Zuckmayer, as Sargent holds Tuesday in his arms, he suddenly stumbles on the idea for his greatest composition, 'The Kiss.' How would a painter react in those circumstances? What exact phraseology would he employ?"

"To herald an inspiration, you mean?" I pondered. "Well, I always smite my forehead and use a simple Greek word—eureka."

Fruitwell ripped off his smock and flung it at his agent. "And for this you fly me from the Coast, you muzzler," he snarled. "Any coffeepot could of told you that!" Suffused with outrage, he stalked to the door, pulverized me and my artifacts with a glance, and was gone. Monroe scampered after him, his face stricken.

Gallwise stood immobilized an instant. Then, swallowing painfully, he folded the smock into the dispatch case like a somnambulist and crossed to the threshold. The crucified smile he turned on me was purest Fra Angelico. "Temperament," he apologized. "But don't be afraid, Mr. Zuckmayer—there won't be a trace of it on the screen. The kid's a great trouper."

It was such nirvana, standing there tranquilly in the dusk after he had left, that I let the phone ring for a full minute. I knew who it was, and my parfait was complete without a Bessarabian cherry, but I also knew Vetlugin's tenacity. I picked up the receiver.

"It's me, Tovarisch." He spoke in such a conspiratorial whisper that for a moment I had trouble distinguishing him. "Look, which painting should I give Mr. Hubris?" he asked breathlessly. "He says he deserves a big one, on account of the publicity you'll get from the film. I claim—"

"I'll settle it." I cut him short. "Call him to the phone."

"But I said you were working—I had orders not to disturb—"

"I've finished," I said. "It's catharsis time."

And it was.

Monomania,
You and Me Is Quits

My immediate reaction when a head studded with aluminum rheostats confronted me over the garden gate last Tuesday morning was one of perplexity. That it belonged to a courier from outer space was, I felt, improbable, for nobody of such transcendent importance would have chosen a weedy Pennsylvania freehold to land on. Its features, moreover, were much too traditional for an interplanetary nuncio; instead of the elephant ears and needle-sharp proboscis that science fiction had prepared me for, the apparition exhibited a freckled Slavic nose and wattles ripened by frequent irrigations of malt. In the same instant, as I straightened up, giddy with the effort of extricating a mullein from the cucumbers, I realized that the spiny coiffure was in actuality a home permanent and the bulging expanse of gingham below it the rest of Mrs. Kozlich, our current cleaning woman.

"I hope I didn't scare you," she said tremulously, "but I thought I better drive over and speak to you personally. Something funny happened while you and the missus were away last weekend." She cast a quick, nervous glance about the surrounding eighty-three acres and lowered her voice. "A man burned a chair on your place Friday night."

"Yes, I know," I replied. "I meant to call you so you wouldn't be alar—"

"I was so frightened I almost fainted," she pursued, unheeding. "My niece Kafka and I were washing your upstairs windows around five o'clock when this station wagon came up the lane. I figured it was yours."

"It was mine, Mrs. Kozlich," I gentled her. "Listen to me, will you? I made a special trip back from the city—on purpose—to *burn* that chair. Do you understand?"

It was obvious she didn't, or, even if she did, was determined not to be denied the opportunity of a dramatic recital. The car, she went on breathlessly, had traversed a long field adjacent to the barn, parking by the gulch where I file old paint cans, leaky gutters, and window screens for future reference. The driver (who bore a striking resemblance to me, the ladies decided from their distant vantage point) had then unloaded a large black easy chair, systematically disemboweled its upholstery, and, while they watched spellbound, set fire to it. "Go back there and look, if you don't believe me," she challenged. "The springs are laying all over the ground where he kicked them. After he drove out, I sent Kafka up and she found a couple of scraps like horsehide or something. It must have been a leather chair."

It was indeed, but what Mrs. Kozlich had witnessed, and what I prudently decided not to spell out for her, was the end of a dream—a romantic quest that began some twenty-two years ago. Just when or how my yearning for a tufted black leather armchair originated I cannot remember. Perhaps some elderly member of the Rhode Island medical profession, which I supported singlehanded as a boy, had one in his consulting room, or I may have seen the prototype, spavined with use, in the professorial chambers at Brown. At any rate, among the fantasies I nurtured into manhood—a princely income and a sleek, piratical schooner for cruising the Great Barrier Reef, to mention only two—was a clearcut image of my ideal study. Its appointments varied from time to time; on occasion the walls were booklined, or hung with rare trophies like Mrs. Gray's lechwe or a sitatunga, or again bare except for a few gems of Impressionist painting. The focus, the keystone of the décor, nonetheless, never varied—a capacious, swollen club chair, well polished, into whose depths one sank and somniferously browsed through the latest English review. There might be a revolving mahogany bookcase alongside, but I wasn't sure. I was afraid it might detract from the rich, baroque impact of the chair.

By the time I had acquired my own inglenook in the mid-thirties, though, and started prowling the auction rooms for my fictive *fauteuil*, I discovered it was a chimera. Curiosities of that sort, dealers pityingly confided, had vanished with the buffalo lap robe and congress gaiters. They offered me substitutes that awoke my outrage—knobby monstrosities of red plastic that tilted at the touch of a spring, slippery leatherette abstractions that pitchforked one into prenatal discomfort inches off the floor. The more I insisted, the more derisive they became. "Look, Grover Cleveland," one of them finally snapped at me after my third approach. "Harmoniums and water wings, diavolos and pungs we got, but Victorian easy chairs—*nyet*. And now, excuse me, will you? I have another nudnick here wants a round table like King Arthur's."

The first intimation that my will-o'-the-wisp, however unattainable, did in fact still exist came in 1938. Yawning through a Tim McCoy Western at a rural cinema in our township, I was suddenly electrified by the furnishings of the sheriff's office. Beside the period roll-top desk stood a voluptuously padded arm-chair, not only covered in black leather but (tears rose to my eyes) its outlines accented by brass nailheads. I whipped to my feet. "That's it! That's it!" I fluted, my voice gone contralto with agitation. "That's my chair!" I was so overwhelmed, to be candid, that it required the intervention of the manager to persuade me to resume my seat, and subsequent accounts, gleaned by my wife from local tradespeople, hinted I had succumbed to a Holy Roller seizure. Undaunted, I took care to note the production details of the film against some future visit to Hollywood, and chancing to be there shortly, at once proceeded to track down the chair. It was relatively simple. In a matter of minutes, Columbia's art department disclosed the name of the warehouse that supplied such props, and, cramming my pockets with enough rhino to vanquish any obstacle, I pelted over. The manager of the enterprise, a foxy-nose with a serried gray marcel that mounted like a linotype keyboard, was the soul of courtesy.

"Of course I remember the piece," he acknowledged smoothly. "This way, please." The freight elevator discharged us in a shadowy loft on the sixth floor, where furniture of every conceivable epoch lay stored. He dove into the maze and yanked aside a dust cover. "There," he said. "Is this the one you mean?"

An inexpressible radiance suffused me. The chair was so much more beautiful than my cinematic memory that speech was inadequate. It was a haven, a refuge; I saw myself lolling in it, churchwarden poised, evolving new cosmogonies, quoting abstruse references to Occam's razor and Paley's watch. "Oh, God," I choked, extracting a fistful of bills. "I—You've made me so happy! How much?"

"How much what?" he asked woodenly.

I explained that I was prepared to buy it, to buy the whole warehouse if necessary. He uttered a sharp, sardonic hoot and bade me wipe my chin. "Not for sale, buddy," he said, replacing its shroud. "You know what this thing brings in every year in rentals? Why, last month alone it worked in *Addled Saddles, Drums Along the Yazoo*—"

Short of manacling myself to the chair, I used every inducement I could marshal to obtain it, including bribery, pleas of medical need, and threats of legal duress, but the chap was intractable. I retired so crushed in spirit that I inclined to be somewhat paranoid about the subject over the ensuing decade. The world supply of tufted black leather, I frequently told my friends, was being manipulated by a small ring of interior decorators, men who would stick at nothing to bilk me. I was telling it to one of them, an advertising nabob and self-admitted expert in arranging the impossible, at a Turkish bath, when he brought me up short.

"Wait a minute," said Broomhead imperiously.

"Outside of Hollywood or the Reform Club, are any of these chairs still extant?"

"Yes, in Washington," I said. "They've some honeys in the Senate corridors—the real McCoy, so to speak—but nobody could ever wangle—"

He produced a solid-gold pencil the diameter of a needle from his towel and scrawled a note on a masseur. "Relax," he commanded. "Your worries are over. I happen to know a politico or two down there who'd go pretty...far...out of his way to accommodate Curt Broomhead."

I automatically dismissed the assertion as bluster, until his secretary phoned me a month later. A certain Mr. X, whom it was inadvisable to identify, in an equally mysterious government bureau, was laid up with croup. On his recovery, he would promptly expedite the item requested by Mr. Tuftola, which, she whispered, was the pseudonym her boss had adopted for the transaction. While elated at the news, I experienced a vague malaise. It bothered me that some fine old lawgiver, a chivalrous Southerner out of George Cable, with a white imperial and arthritis, might be unceremoniously deposed from his chair because of my whim. I was also positive that I had heard a muffled click during our phone conversation, as though the line were bugged. Before I could cry peccavi and tout Broomhead off, however, the affair took on juggernaut momentum. Telegrams and messages proliferated, warning me that Mr. X's favor was in transit, and I received unmistakable assurance from a Chinese fortune cookie that destiny was arranging a surprise. A fortnight thence, two orangutans in expressmen's aprons dumped a formidable crate on the sidewalk outside our New York brownstone. After an ugly jurisdictional squabble, they departed, leaving the handyman and me to wrestle the shipment up three flights; after an uglier one, we did so, and he departed, leaving me to open it. I was ablaze with fever and salivating freely as I hacked through the excelsior wrappings, but I cooled off fast enough. Inside was a stiff and dismal board-room chair, welted with tacks, that belonged in a third-rate loan shark's office. The sticker on the reverse, however, implied otherwise. It read, "Property of U.S. State Dept."

To adduce proof that the husky, straw-hatted young man in gabardine who tailed me the whole next month was an F.B.I. operative is impossible, nor can I swear that my mail was fluoroscoped during that period. I do know that for a while I underwent all the tremors of a Graham Greene character on the run, even if it had no purificatory effect on my religious views. When my funk abated sufficiently to donate the chair to a charity bazaar, I arrived at a decision. The only way I could possibly attain my ideal was to have it custom made, and to that end I embarked on a secret layaway plan at the Coiners' and Purloiners' National. Early last summer, I took the accrual to a wholesaler friend in the Furniture Design Center, along with a steel engraving that embodied every curlicue I lusted for. He examined it tolerantly.

"It's your money, Sidney," he said, "but if I were you, I'd look around the auction rooms—"

I flung my hat on his showroom floor and stamped on it like Edgar Kennedy. "Stop!" I screamed. "Duplicate that chair and keep your Goddam advice to yourself! If I need advice, I'll go to a shrinker!"

"You're overdue now," he observed, picking up a hassock to ward me off. "Okey-doke. It'll take six weeks. And don't call for it," he added quickly. "We'll deliver."

The result was not a masterpiece, as one applies the term to a floral group by Odilon Redon or the mosaics in the Naples Museum, but it ran a close second. It was a paragon of cozy chairs, a marvel of the most intricate tufting, a monument to the upholsterer's art. You sank into its refulgent black bosom and were instantly permeated with *douceur de vivre* such as you had never known. Apothegms worthy of La Rochefoucauld tumbled from your lips, full-fashioned epigrams pleading to be encased in boxes in *McCall's* and *Reader's Digest*. True, it was a difficult chair to slumber in; at the beginning, its magnificence overawed me and I sat gingerly in it, holding at eye level a copy of Sir Samuel Baker's *The Albert Nyanza* in crushed levant. I then tried browsing through the latest English review, but somehow couldn't get past the pictures of Ovomalt and thermal underwear. At last, I found the key in Max Lerner's windy periods, and, lapped in his peristaltic rhetoric, slept like a baby. Once inside that chair, Lerner in hand, I was as remote from hypertension as from the Asiatic capitals where he bombinated.

When Buddha smiles and all is cotton candy, though, it is axiomatic that one edges toward the nearest cyclone cellar. Following a blissful week, my wife and I motored off to Willimantic to pick up a few spools of vintage thread. En route, she informed me that in our absence a new domestic had been instructed to give the flat a thorough cleaning. The place fairly gleamed when we tottered in the door; the rugs had been shampooed, the silver was burnished to diamond brilliance, and the furniture sparkled with a million highlights. As I stood openmouthed, like one of the carp at Fontainebleau, my wife issued from the kitchen, brandishing a note and a clotted paintbrush.

"A treasure! A dreamboat!" she chortled. "Guess what that girl did! She shellacked all the tables, even the breadboard and the stepladder! She worked two whole nights—"

"W-why is that sheet draped over my comfy chair?" I quavered.

"To protect it, stupid," she said impatiently. "I'm going to double her salary tomorrow, sign her to a lifetime contract—"

I leaped past her, whisked away the sheet, and was presented with a spectacle beyond description, beyond contemplation. The leather was piebald, marbleized with a scaly armor plate of orange-and-gray shellac bonded onto its surface for eternity. Never, even among the tortured vinyl-and-zebra abominations in the lowest borax showroom on East Eighth Street, had I beheld anything so loathsome. With a great cry, I sank to my knees, and, nuzzling one bulbous armrest, burst into racking sobs. Half an hour afterward, I slung a five-gallon can of kerosene into the rear of our wagon, unmindful that it splattered the aspiration of a lifetime. Then I slammed up the tailgate and headed grimly downtown toward the Holland Tunnel.

Dry Run—Everybody Down!

...Warner financing was arranged for the movie [*The Old Man and the Sea*], and Hemingway was given an advance of $175,000. The author suggested that Peter Viertel, whose work he knew, write the screen play. Hemingway wanted Viertel, as part of his conditioning, to live for a while in a primitive Cuban fishing shack and to spend an equal amount of time handling a native fishing dory, single-handed, against the turbulent currents and under the blazing 120-degree summer sun of the Gulf Stream. Viertel surprised everyone (except, perhaps, Hemingway) by surviving this tropical ordeal, and, later, completed the script in New York.—*From an article by Halsey Raines in the* Times.

Oilskins agleam, his orangutan eyes glittering at the prospect of baksheesh, the doorman of the Ganymede bent forward into my taxi, plucked me from it like a walnut meat, and expertly tilted his umbrella to funnel the maximum of rain down my collar. "Great weather for ducks," he whickered, all greasy bonhomie. I rewarded him with a smile negotiable at any frozen-food locker and circled past into the lobby. At the desk, a sallow ramrod in a regimental necktie that could have denoted His Majesty's Seventh Imperturbables mantled his forehead in disdain when I asked for Mort

211

Schrift.

"Would he be expecting you, perchance?" he inquired, struggling to master his incredulity. I examined his cravat as though it were a lizard, and said briefly that I was a client of the man. "Suite 647," he disclosed, producing a small box, "and you might take along this parcel from Dunhill's that just arrived. It's his special mixture—I happen to know he needs it quite urgently."

"Gee whillikins!" I said. "I hope he can hold out till I get there."

"That I'll guarantee you," he returned spitefully.

Shriveling him to ash with a glance (though I daresay he may have twitched spasmodically for a while), I stalked toward the elevators. The other occupants of my car were a pair of tall, willowy thoroughbreds apparently checking in from Oshkosh, for they were flanked by luggage, the color of a weathered skull, of every conceivable size. From the scorn they evinced, I sensed that they were unaccustomed to persons bearing packages, so I receded as far as I was able into the costly woodwork. The coryphee who opened the door of Schrift's antechamber, a Dresden-china shepherdess with scallops of blue-black hair framing her face, looked like the secretaries he generally used on his lightning visits from the Coast—more adept at disengaging a zipper at the Copa than at shorthand. She uttered a happy squeak at the sight of the parcel.

"You finally brought it!" she cried. "We were calling up all morning! Here, wait till I get some change—"

I explained, rather frigidly, that I was no delivery boy but a business associate, who, at Schrift's entreaty, had trekked from the Pennsylvania bush in a torrential downpour, and that unless given instant audience I had other fish to fry. "Is he up yet?" I demanded.

"Well—er—I think so," she said evasively. "I mean, he didn't get in till four. He hosted a party at Neuralgio's for our new French author, Claude Nasal-Passages, and then everybody went on to the Twelve Apostles."

"In that case," I growled, but rhetoric withered on my lips. Clad in primrose-yellow pajamas the breast pocket of which bore a large fleur-de-lis and his initials in soutache, Schrift leaped from the bedroom and caught me in a hammerlock. So emotional was his welcome and so astringent his cologne that I was nearly undone. After all, it was almost two years since he had become my agent in Hollywood, and while he had never earned me even a picayune, I still viewed him as my genie in embryo. "I had a hell of a time getting here, brother," I revealed when we had finished trading insincerities. "I hope it's not the usual wild-goose chase."

"Pops," declaimed Schrift, one hand on his soutache and the other raised like Richelieu, "this much I'll tell you. We stand on the threshold of such loot that it frightens me. Piastres—yellow doubloons—the wealth of the Indies! But first there must be coffee," he said, spinning toward his odalisque. "Don't stand there— bring coffee, toast, the papers! And get John Huston on the phone."

"In Galway?" she queried uncertainly.

"Galway," he groaned. "He was in Galway *yesterday*; today he's in Cuzco. Wait—on second thought, never

213

mind; I'll see him Thursday at Klosters. Here, baby," he said, turning back to me, "come in the bedroom while I dress. Larry Olivier's waiting for me at the Pavilion, and you know how he hates to be hung up." I didn't, but I realized that to expect preferential treatment over a knight would be absurd, especially since I had lost face with Schrift by hastening to his summons, and I complied meekly. Dispersing the hillock of galley proofs and playscripts on a twin bed, my genie bade me sit, and vanished into a closet. To judge by the bounteous wardrobe he had imported for his forty-eight-hour visit, he evidently planned to run the social gamut. Even the mantelpiece, I observed with wonder, held a quartet of sports caps in various arresting tweeds, all cinctured at the brim by minuscule leather belts. A moment later, Schrift reappeared in a striking pair of undershorts, with vertical stripes like French wallpaper. "Now, for openers," he began, extracting the trees from a pair of suède chukker boots, "did you read this new best seller *Valuta*, by Waldemar Knobnose!"

"Only the first eighteen pages," I admitted. "The woman whose copy it was got off the bus at Altman's."

"Well, you missed a great literary experience, catharsiswise," he said. "It's going to make the hottest picture in the annals of the industry, and you, lover"— he stabbed his index finger at me forcefully—"are going to adapt it for the screen. At a prince's ransom."

"Sounds tempting," I said, making no effort to conceal my skepticism, "but there's one detail you forget—censorship. A romance between a nine-year-old bank auditor and a female cashier six times his age? Show me one Hollywood producer who'd dare to make a movie of that."

"O.K., wisenheimer, I will," chortled Schrift, in triumph. "I closed a deal for it at three o'clock yesterday with Jerry GeWald himself! Four hundred and thirty thousand smackers, plus eight per cent of the gross!"

"And he intends to follow the story just as it stands!" I asked doubtfully.

"Down to the smallest financial and emotional *drehdel*," he swore. "The audience'll see every Goddam roll of pennies she steals—they'll quiver with him as he strives to reconcile her debits, as their totals accidentally brush, as passion is born. Then the midnight orgies around the adding machine in the deserted cage, where she plies him with drugged brownies, and their cross-country flight through the entire banking system till she loses him to that little blond tramp of a C.P.A. Yes, sirree, GeWald's going to film it all, and he's hungry for you to do the screenplay, regardless of fee."

"Then what's the hitch?" I demanded, mindful of the worm that lurked somewhere in his golden apple.

"Look at this shirt!" exclaimed Schrift, with sudden irrelevant fury. "Specially made for me by Thresher & Glenny in London—it cost more than you probably spent on coal last winter. If I told 'em once, I told 'em a hundred times—I want the monogram in Old *English*, not roman type! What do they think I am—a letterhead? No wonder the British Empire's falling apart."

"Getting back to *Valuta*," I reminded him gently, "who does GeWald have in mind for the leads? Now that Freddie Bartholomew's shaving, there may be trouble casting the boy auditor."

"Ah, we don't have to stick to the book too literally," he said carelessly. "I'd buy any good juvenile in the part—like Donald O'Connor, say, or Paul Newman. Then your cashier, I see her as a little younger dame—a Julie Newmar, or Cyd Charisse with a silver rinse. The main thing is to preserve the *spirit* of the novel, which is why Knobnose, the author, wants you to work in a bank first. GeWald's set up the whole thing for you, the job and everything—"

"One sec," I interjected. "You mean I have to take a fiscal to qualify for the assignment?"

"Don't blow your stack, for crisake," implored Schrift from the depths of the pullover he was squirming into. "It's just to condition you—to help you dig the psychology of the characters. You merely go and spend a month or so behind the wicket, handling bills of different denominations, chaffing depositors, and like that. It's a friendly little family bank in Sphagnum, New Jersey—the Peculators' & Predators' National."

"It isn't going to be all that simple," I demurred. "To really steep myself in the boy's point of view, I'd have to live the role—dress the way he does, play with trains, even contract measles."

"Nah, just put on knickerbockers and get rid of the mustache" he advised. "Those squares over in Jersey'll never tumble—their kids look like old men anyway. Well," he said, knotting a Paisley kerchief under his blazer, "I'm glad you kindled to the idea, and I know you'll do a sensational script if I can sell Olivier on you."

"Olivier?" I repeated. "Where does he fit into the

picture?"

"He doesn't yet, but he will when we get through lunch," predicted Schrift confidently. "It's a terrific vehicle for him. Can you imagine a marquee reading '*Valuta*, with Sir Laurence Olivier'? Man, would that bring in the people !"

"Even in a rainstorm," I agreed, rising. "And, speaking of bringing in people in a rainstorm, the next time you dare to call me and suggest—"

As oblivious as though I were speaking Urdu, Schrift whisked up the phone, cuddled it in his shoulder, and fired a volley of orders at his handmaiden off-scene. They involved a multiplicity of names of such theatrical luster—Moss and Noël, Leland and Abe, George and Josh—that my grievance trailed off into a peevish whine. Capping his monologue with a command to rush Marlene a dozen orchids and break their dinner date, Schrift swung about peremptorily. "What's it doing outside?" he barked.

"Why—er—I—I guess it's still teeming, Mort," I said, in an unexpected falsetto that was deeply humiliating.

"Hmm," he observed with a frown. "Good thing I brought my rainwear from the Coast." He plunged into the closet and emerged with an armful of mackintoshes, slickers, and waterproofs of various weights. Selecting a heavy rubberized garment ideally suited to the Brazilian rain forest, he slipped into it and crossed to the mantelpiece. For a moment, he stood indecisive before the array of tweed caps; then, donning one scarcely larger than a wheat cake, he tightened its surcingle and threw me a crisp nod. "Come along," he commanded. "You can walk me down the lobby."

Our descent, somnambulistic as any of Beebe's to the ocean floor, was devoid of incident except for one moment at the elevator. As the doors clashed open to admit us, I was confronted by the same patrician couple, surrounded by their osseous luggage, with whom I had risen earlier. They had apparently stood there, transfixed and endlessly levitating, the whole time—unless, of course, they were waxworks arranged by the management to lend chic to the premises. Schrift, immersed in a wad of cables and correspondence, paid them no heed, merely emitting an occasional yelp of gratification or anguish at some coup or setback.

Once on the sidewalk, he suddenly recollected my existence and seized my hand in a grip so convulsive that it almost brought me to my knees. "Keep in touch, now," he rapped out, "and whatever you do, stay near the phone. The way this deal's developing, I may need you in the middle of the night." He nimbly sidestepped a basset hound that had wound itself about his ankles, and, with a wave, pelted off toward Madison.

I've eaten and slept by the phone ever since, but thus far no word. I suspect they've hired Peter Viertel for the post, and quite properly. Be it in quest of a marlin or a defalcation, he's twice the man I am.

Baby, I Will Enchant Thine Ear— Maybe

Call me uxorious, spoony, passion's plaything, but let a woman signify her whim by so much as a nod and, by George, I'll climb the highest mountain, swim the deepest ocean to gratify it. While the climbing and swimming this compulsion has entailed would stagger credulity, they're piffling compared to what I underwent recently in Europe to obtain a pair of earrings. Chronologically, the affair began last spring with a trivial observation of my wife's—one of those remarks that drop like a seed into the subconscious and germinate there over an entire summer. Halfway through a novel of David Garnett's she was reading, Madame looked up reflectively. "Remember that garnet brooch of mine?" she asked. "It's back in fashion again. Don't you think I ought to get a pair of earrings to match?" The only response she got was an indulgent chuckle from behind my newspaper, which was rather unaccountable, since I lay dozing a good ten feet away from it. At any rate, six months later I was in London after a protracted stay abroad, faced with the problem of a suitable homecoming gift. The usual pattern of perfume, sweaters, and Liberty squares seemed so deadly that I resolved to vary it, and betook myself to the Caledonian Market, that great repository of antiques, bric-a-brac, and pinchbeck in Bermondsey. For well over an hour, I rummaged through stalls laden with Victorian knickknacks, pewter, china, cutlery, glass, and miscellaneous rubbish of every description from passementerie to doorknobs, erotic nutcrackers to scrimshaw. Somewhere in this magpie's nest, I told myself with decreasing assurance, there must be a keepsake worthy of my spouse. A drophead sewing machine? The woman bought all her clothes from Dior. A sphygmometer? Her pulse never varied a hairbreadth. A wastebasket made from an elephant's foot? She doted on pachyderms, cried unashamedly at Babar. Homeward bound to the West End, I suddenly recollected her wistful reference to the earrings, and raced back to Bermondsey.

"Garnet eardrops, sir?" the dealers echoed as one man. "Shouldn't think you'd find a pair in England. Fearfully rare. Terribly *vieux jeu*. Nobody fancies them nowadays. Bad luck, they say. See them occasionally on a laundress or a skivvy, sir, but ladies won't have 'em. Sorry, old chap. Have you tried Torquay? Bournemouth? Blackpool? Ah, yes, for a costume party, no doubt. Haven't the foggiest, old man. Pawnshop near Ludgate Circus, but I wouldn't promise. For a *young* woman, you said, sir? Sorry, old boy."

Overwhelmed by futility, I was about to abandon the quest when a cherry-nosed beldam in a man's cap and rope-knit sweater came to my rescue. The only place that might conceivably handle such an item, she said, detaching an inch of Woodbine from her lip, was a shop near the British Museum whose stock of Edwardian jewelry was unrivaled. Be it a stomacher or a diamond garter, it could be found at Intaglio's; all the gentry, added my tarnished angel deferentially, traded there. In less time than it takes to leaf through *Burke's Peerage and Baronetage*, I sped to Bloomsbury, found the shop, and communicated my needs to the gentlewoman presiding over it. She gave me the weary smile one reserves for eccentrics, and produced half a dozen trays containing unimaginable splendors. Trinkets of sapphire, emerald, ruby, jade, fire opal, and every semiprecious stone except the garnet coruscated through her fingers, all mounted in settings antedating the Boer War. After doing her utmost to sell me a blue carbuncle choker, a sunburst studded with rose diamonds, and a pearl dog collar worn by the fifth Marchioness of Londonderry, my saleslady threw in the towel. "Personally, I think you're on a wild-goose chase," she declared. "Of course, you can always insert an advert in the agony column of the *Times*. I'm sure if you offered a couple of hundred quid—"

"Wait a minute," I said, realizing that I was in danger of succumbing to an expensive monomania. "Maybe garnets *are* a trifle démodé, at that. What do you have in a good, inexpensive scarab?"

With a click of dentures that graphically expressed her opinion of all tourists, and redskins in particular, she slid a trayful of scarabs toward me. I selected one I felt would blend nicely with any of my wife's blouses, especially those starched in Reckitt's Blue, and bore it away. Almost immediately, a couple of disturbing, seemingly unrelated incidents occurred that made me wonder whether I had unwittingly involved myself in one of Carol Reed's gaudier thrillers. Entering my hotel room about teatime the next day, I surprised a valet half submerged in the closet, ostensibly draping pants on a hanger. In response to my query, he gave me some curious, evasive answer to the effect that he had discovered them on the floor. As he withdrew, I was struck by his sphinxlike smile and the fact that his features had a distinctly Egyptian cast. Could his visit have had an ulterior motive, I asked myself, startled— my scarab, possibly? The tissue it was wrapped in appeared untouched, but I could have sworn the elastic had been tampered with. In the automatic elevator that very same evening, though, I had an encounter the significance of which was unmistakable. The car had hardly started upward when my nostrils detected the characteristic scent of some Oriental perfume like sandalwood. I turned and received a coup d'oeil from a pair of sloe eyes berimmed with kohl. The impact was so abrupt, their air of invitation so unabashed, that it was a moment before I had a chance to discreetly survey the owner. She was a ravishing Eurasian, her lissome figure swathed in sables and her sensuous lips curled in a mocking pout—Sax Rohmer's Kâramanèh to the life. In a trice, I saw through the whole design. Having failed to purloin my scarab, the ring in Cairo had detailed her to lure me to some unsavory grogshop in Wapping Old Stairs with a trapdoor opening conveniently into the Thames. A moment's irresolution and I would be done for, another unsolved file in Scotland Yard. I returned an equally mocking smile to the fair decoy and pressed the emergency button. "Queen's gambit declined, my gazelle," I said grimly, and descended. Her utter bafflement was comical in the extreme.

The precautions I now took to secrete the scarab, unfortunately, were so devious that I ended by losing it altogether, and with my departure imminent, the need for a present was crucial. The annual Kensington Antiques Fair, by a coincidence, was just concluding, and I determined to make a final search there for the earrings. To my immoderate joy, a handsome pair turned up in the second booth I visited—large, shapely garnets backed by silver filigree and a warranty from Mr. Plimsoll, the dealer, that they were at least a hundred years old. Mr. Plimsoll won my heart instantly—a gentle sexagenarian with silver hair and exquisite manners, the sort of elderly curate who populates English plays that fold in two nights. His scrupulousness especially endeared him to me; he insisted on retaining the earrings, even though I had paid for them, so that he could replace a somewhat flawed stone. "Nonsense, my dear fellow," he said, waving aside my protests. "I wouldn't dream of letting your good wife wear these unless they were letter-perfect. Take a day or two to pop in another garnet, but I'll fetch 'em around to your hotel in plenty of time before you leave. Here's my card, and may I say in passing that I consider your countrymen the salt of the earth?"

Well, I couldn't help choking up at that, and we had a pretty emotional parting, wringing each other's hand and so forth, but when four days went by and no Plimsoll, I began to get restive. Since the Kensington Fair had closed meanwhile, I tried phoning him at his place of business, and learned, with agitation, that no such number existed. After a nightmare bus journey involving three changes, I at length reached the address in Peckham Rye, the suburb of outer London where the shop was supposedly located. Nobody, needless to say, had ever heard of my antiquary. En route back to the hotel through endless mean streets, I consigned Plimsoll to the seventh ring of purgatory and, with a pinch or two of sophistry, effectively settled my gift problem. After all, it wasn't really the gift so much as the spirit, et cetera—and besides, my wife had probably forgotten the earrings long since. Ultimately, at my own convenience, I'd buy her an ounce of perfume, a sweater, and a Liberty square, and *Schluss*. If they were good enough for her grandmother, they were good enough for her. And anyhow, why were women so importunate nowadays? I became so worked up by the time we got to Marble Arch that I very nearly decided to bring her nothing at all.

I almost did, thanks to my precious Mr. Plimsoll. Late that afternoon, as I was strolling along Shaftesbury Avenue, I saw him jauntily cross the zebra swinging a dispatch case, sanctimonious as damn all with his silver locks fluttering in the wind. I shouted after him to stop. He threw me a frightened glance and took off in the direction of Great Windmill Street. For a man of his years, he showed amazing stamina, and I was well-nigh beat when he abruptly ducked into the Nosh Bar, a delicatessen close by. I pounded in after him, naturally, creating quite a tableau among the patrons munching their salt-beef sandwiches and drinking lemon tea, but do you know, he'd vanished without a trace. I was certain he must have slipped out the rear entrance, until the proprietor finally managed to satisfy me that he hadn't any. Maybe there was a trapdoor or something, like those in the grogshops at Wapping Old Stairs; I still can't figure out where the old bleeder went.

But that wasn't the last of him by a long chalk, and it fair makes me break into a muck sweat to think of what ensued. Two nights later, alighting from a cab in front of a music hall in Hammersmith, I spotted Plimsoll, bold as brass, lounging by the stage door with a cigar in his teeth. (At least, I think it was Plimsoll; if not, it was his twin brother.) Anyway, he caught sight of me simultaneously, and whipped like a rabbit into a passage alongside the theater. I gave chase, and, hot on his heels, found myself on a steep incline. It must have led into some sort of basement under the stage or thereabouts, because I glimpsed a costume rack and a lot of electrical gear in transit, but I was too distracted hunting for Plimsoll to pay much heed. Suddenly I heard a voice yell, "Hey, there, mate, don't tread on that!" and, glancing down, saw that I had stepped on a small wooden platform almost flush with the floor. Whatever took place in the next few seconds happened so swiftly that I can still hardly credit it. With a sickening lurch, the platform shot upward, carrying me with it, and as I cowered to protect my head I heard a deafening fanfare, climaxing in a crash of cymbals. For a moment, I was too dazzled by the flood of candlepower illuminating me to distinguish anything; then I made out a row of footlights dead ahead, and beyond it an infinity of grinning faces, tier on tier. Overcome at the realization that I had been elevated to stardom, I turned to flee, and felt a sinewy hand grip my arm. A tall, suave individual in evening clothes, his Mephistophelean eyebrows heightened by makeup, was bathing me in a smile not altogether devoid of menace. "Steady on, my beauty," he purred. "Just relax and let Scarpini the Great waft you into the Elysian fields."

"I don't want to be wafted," I squeaked, crimson with embarrassment. "Look, Mister, there's some mistake—I'm not in show biz—"

"Neither am I," he said glibly. "This is merely a little scientific experiment to demonstrate the power of mind over matter. Just stretch out on the table here and keep your eye on the shiny object in my hand."

"I won't, I tell you!" I panted, backing away.

"Oh, yes, you will," he said, with a catlike smile. "Now, down you go, you willful boy, and lie still. You're sleepy...you're getting sleepier..."

To retain your composure under stress is tough enough, but when you're forcibly levitated into the horizontal and a spiv in a rented dress suit starts passing hoops around you, you can't very well behave like Lord Louis Mountbatten. The orchestral din was such, furthermore, and the applause so shattering, that my pleas to Scarpini to lower me, to release the mechanism or whatever the hell was holding me, went unheard. Eventually—I wouldn't know how—I made my escape into the wings, and, limp as a rag, crept to the nearest cab rank. Speaking as a man who'd practically relived "The 39 Steps," the balance of my London sojourn was pretty humdrum. I spent the whole time in bed, except for a quick trip to the Burlington Arcade, where I bought Milady a nice woolen steamer shawl five feet long. It's the kind of fleece you won't get anywhere else in Britain—unless you run into Plimsoll, that is. If you do, tell him I'll catch up with him yet.

Impresario on the Lam

The voice that came over the wire last Thursday was full of gravel and Hollywood subjunctives. It was a voice trained to cut through the din of night clubs and theater rehearsals, a flexible instrument that could shift from adulation to abuse in a syllable, ingratiating yet peremptory, a rich syrup of unction and specious authority. "Listen, Clyde, you don't know me from a hole in the ground," it began with deadly accuracy, "but I'm the agent for a friend of yours, Morris Flesh." Before I could disavow ever having heard of Flesh, his representative had washed his hands of him and was scuttling down the fairway. "I've got a client deeply interested in putting on a revue," he confided. "A smart, intimate show that kids the passing scene, the various fads and foibles like television and mah-jongg and psychoanalysis—dig me ? Morris recommends you to pen the sketches, and while I personally would rather have a name, I'm willing to gamble on his opinion. Now, here's the score, Pops. My backer is strictly from Dixie, a peasant from the tall rhubarbs. I'm running the creative side and this is what I have in mind." I laid the receiver gently on the desk and went out to lunch.

228

When I returned two hours later, the monologue was purling on as inexorably as the Blue Nile. "This girl composer has got Vassar in an uproar, baby," the voice was affirming. "She's the hottest thing that ever hit Poughkeepsie—another Cole Porter, only younger. Sophisticated but simple at the same time." I hung up, and dialing the business office, vanished into the limbo of unlisted telephone subscribers.

Though not constitutionally averse to the crackle of greenbacks, I learned many years ago—twenty-eight, in fact—that of all the roads to insolvency open to my profession, entanglement in a revue is the shortest. Every revue since *The Garrick Gaieties* has been hatched from the same larva, an impassioned declaration by some seer flushed with Martinis that what Broadway needs this season is a smart, intimate show like *The Garrick Gaieties*. In 1932, Poultney Kerr, a onetime yacht broker riding out the depression on a cask of brandy, said it with such persistence that a group of idealists gave him a hundred thousand dollars to demonstrate, and he did so with a *cauchemar* called *Sherry Flip*. Kerr's qualifications as a producer, apart from a honeyed tongue, were minimal. His executive ability was pitiful, his judgment paltry, and his equilibrium unstable in crisis. He did, nevertheless, look the big wheel—a corpulent, natty man given to Homburg hats and carnations in the buttonhole, with the classic empurpled nose of the *bon vivant* and a talent for imbibing oceans of Courvoisier without crumpling. I met him at a low ebb in my fortunes and left him at a lower. In between, I got so concentrated a dose of hysteria and wormwood that I still quail at the mention of sherry.

S J Perelman

At a moment when my wallet was at its flabbiest, the
project started in the classic tradition with an urgent
phone call from Lytton Swazey, a lyric writer I had
known casually around the doughnut shop in Times
Square we both frequented. Could I, he asked, confer
with him and his composer that afternoon at Kerr's
apartment about an upcoming revue patterned after
The Garrick Gaieties? I blacked my shoes in a flash and
pelted over. The portents seemed dazzling. Swazey,
after years of grinding out special material for willowy
chanteuses in cocktail bars, had recently teamed up
with a Russian composer named Herman Earl.
Together they had confected a valiseful of show tunes,
and it was on these, plus the half-dozen sketches I
would supply, that *Sherry Flip* was to be based.

It may have been wishful thinking that warped my
perspective, or a greenhorn's superstitious awe of song
writers as demigods, but Swazey had hardly bawled out
a couple of ballads before I put down my glass and
emotionally announced, "Gentlemen, count me in."
Needless to say, our sponsor was not outraged by my
quick assent. He plied me with flattery and cognac,
hailed me as a theatrical sibyl rivaling Daniel Frohman.
The few tentative ideas for sketches I broached evoked
paroxysms of laughter. "I don't want to put a jinx on it,
boys," exulted Kerr, wrenching the cork from a fresh
bottle of Hennessey, "but I think we've got a hit." What
with all the self-congratulation and the mirage of fat
royalties he conjured up, I agreed to terms that even a
Mexican migrant worker would have flouted, and
bowled off straightaway to Bachrach to be photographed. I figured I might not have the leisure to sit for

him later when I became the toast of Broadway.

Lodged in an airless cubicle in Kerr's offices, I spent the next five weeks chewing licorice fortified with Benzedrine and evolving skits, emerging only to replenish myself with corned-beef sandwiches. *Sherry Flip*, meanwhile, was subtly changing from a collection of grandiose phrases into a living organism. A director, scenic designer, and choreographer materialized; the anteroom boiled with singers and dancers, tumblers and ventriloquists, sister acts and precocious children. Kerr himself preserved a state of Olympian detachment for the most part, huddling with lawyers in his sanctum. There were disquieting whispers that our finances were shaky, but as rehearsal day neared, he secured additional pledges, sounds of wassail again rang through the corridors, and we began work on a note of the most buoyant optimism.

Rehearsals went swimmingly the first fortnight. Not a speck of artistic temperament marked the cast; everyone was bewitched by the vivacity of the score and the brilliance of the sketches. Manners were impeccable, the atmosphere as sunny as a Monet picnic. Then, abruptly, the lid blew off. Halfway through her big solo one afternoon, our prima donna developed an acute attack of paranoia. Derogating the number as an inept Russian plagiarism of "Rio Rita," she declared that she would never sully her reputation by singing it in public. The composer, justifiably stung to fury, flew into a storm of picturesque Muscovite cuss-words. He offered to punch her nose—which, he added parenthetically, was bobbed—and threatened to bring her up before Equity on charges. The director patched up a shaky truce, but the incident had abraded the company's nerves and opened the door to further insubordination. Mysterious excrescences began to appear on the material I had furnished the actors. A diplomatic travesty of mine suddenly blossomed out with a routine in which, using a wallet stuffed with toilet paper, our top banana flimflammed a Polish butcher from Scranton. When I complained, I was told that it had scored a triumph on every burlesque wheel in America. If it offended Percy Bysshe Shelley—as he jocosely referred to me—I could return to writing for the little magazines. The barometer, in short, was falling, there were mutterings in the fo'c'sl, and one didn't have to be Ziegfeld to prophesy that *Sherry Flip* was in for many a squall before it reached port.

By the week prior to the Boston tryout, stilettos were flashing in earnest and the company buzzed like a hive of bees. The comedians, made overweening by victory, had woven a crazy quilt of drolleries and *double-entendres* that made the brain reel. They impersonated androgynes and humorous tramps, thwacked the showgirls' bottoms with rolled-up newspapers, and squirted water from their boutonnieres. Their improvisations totally unnerved Wigmore, the director, an able man around an Ibsen revival but a newcomer to the musical theater. The poor man fluttered about in a continual wax, wringing his hands like ZaSu Pitts and trying to assert his authority. In the dance department, there was a similar lack of co-ordination. The production numbers, two portentous ballets in the style colloquially known as "Fire in a Whorehouse," were being revised from day to day. Muscle-bound youths stamped about bearing dryads who whinnied in ecstasy; shoals of coryphees fled helter-skelter across the stage; and out on the apron, chin cupped in his hand, the choreographer brooded, dreaming up new flights of symbolism. To aggravate matters, a protegée of the composer's, a $55-dollar-a-week soprano with whom he had dallied in good faith, was loudly demanding a featured spot in the show, on pain of divulging the escapade to her husband. Whatever *Sherry Flip* lacked in smartness, its intimacy was unquestionable.

The *estocada*, however, was yet to come. Six o'clock of the evening before our departure for Boston, Murray Zweifel, the company manager, called me aside to retail alarming news—our producer had disappeared. Murray, a Broadway veteran, was on the verge of prostration. "He's quit the show," he said brokenly. "Walked out cold. We're done for." The particulars were simple enough, readily comprehensible to any student of alcohol. Kerr, unmanned by dissension with his backers and loath to open the show on what he contemptuously termed a shoestring, had taken refuge in the grape and abdicated. "The goddam fool is winging," Murray snuffled, grasping my lapels. "You've got to find him and get him on that train, baby. You're the only one who can do it—he won't listen to common sense."

The compliment was equivocal at best, and nine weeks of nightmare tension had taken their toll of me, but I realized that the welfare of sixty-odd folk was at stake, my own among theirs, and I knocked under. Pulling on a pair of waders, I set out to comb the bars that Kerr frequented. About ten-thirty, after a fruitless search of the West Side that extended to the clipjoints of Columbus Avenue, I flushed my man in a blind pig on East 54th Street. He was arm in arm with a prosperous Greek restaurateur from Bellows Falls; they had just consummated a deal to open a chain of diners in Thessaly and were toasting the venture in boilermakers. For all his carousing, Kerr was clear-eyed and crisp as muslin. He embraced me affectionately and insisted we pour a libation on the altar of friendship. The moment I disclosed my purpose, however, he grew violent. He was done with tinsel and sawdust, he declaimed; he wanted no more of the theater and its cut-throat machinations. I tried guile, supplication, and saccharine, but to no avail. Toward midnight, I phoned Zweifel for counsel.

"For crisake don't lose him!" he pleaded. "Feed him a Mickey—anything! If he's not on the nine o'clock to Boston, we're dead!"

"He's an iron man, Murray," I wailed. "He's mixing Scotch, vodka, bourbon—"

"Listen," he broke in. "Dr. Proctor's his physician—he'll cool him out with a sleeping powder! I'll phone him to expect you."

The process of extricating Kerr from the Greek took a full hour and the cunning of serpents. Eventually, though, I prevailed and, a trifle jingled from the soda I had taken in the line of duty, got him to the doctor's flat. A party was in progress, celebrating, I believe, Jenner's epochal discovery of the principle of vaccine, but not all the guests were medical. Out of the haze, I recall a tête-à-tête on a davenport with a blonde in salmon-pink satin, who read my palm and forecast business reverses. The augury cast a chill on our friendship, and moving off, I fell into a long, senseless wrangle about George Antheil with a musician resembling a carp. At intervals, Dr. Proctor's bibulous face swam into my field of vision, giving me conspiratorial winks and assuring me, in tones from outer space, that Kerr was under control. "Chloral hydrate," I heard him intone. "Just a few drops in his glass. He'll cave any time now." Hours later, I remember clinging to some portieres to steady myself while the doctor thickly conceded defeat. "Can't understand it," he said, laboring to focus his eyes. "Enough there to foal an ox. Average person go down like a felled ax. Got to hand it to old Poultney. Hard as nails." I groped past him to a book-lined alcove where Kerr was waltzing cheek to cheek with a cadaverous, sloe-eyed beauty on the order of Jetta Goudal. Now that drugs and entreaty had failed, my only recourse was insult. Castigating him for a yellow-belly and a welsher, I challenged him to redeem himself.

"I dare you to fly up to Boston!" I cried. "I've never been on a plane, but I'll do it if you will. That is," I said witheringly, "if you've got the moxie."

His brow darkened and he discarded the bush-league Eurasian with an oath. "We'll see who's got more moxie," he snarled. "Come along, you little four-eyed shrimp!"

I had won the first round; speeding through deserted streets toward the Newark Airport, my impresario's choler abated and he sank into a light coma. Instinct told me that if I could only lure him aboard the milk plane, his egotism would make him stick till the curtain rose. But Fate was dealing from the bottom of the deck. A dense, pea-soup fog blanketed the field, and the solitary clerk at the terminal held out little promise of improvement. The entire coast was closed in from Hatteras to the Bay of Fundy, he reported, savoring the despair on my face; even the mails were grounded. Kerr, meanwhile, had seized the opportunity to vanish into the washroom, where I found him draining a fifth of gin he had somehow managed to secrete in his clothes. There was only one hope now, to shanghai him back to the morning train; but with no taxi in sight and a bankroll of forty cents, it would obviously take some fancy logistics. Day was breaking when I finally wheedled the driver of a towel-supply truck into dropping us at the nearest subway stop. The ensuing ride into Manhattan unraveled what remained of my ganglia. In his sheltered life, Kerr, it appeared, had never ridden on a subway. He was seized with repugnance for the overalled workmen about him, their unshaven faces and their surly glances, and promptly went pukka sahib.

"Look at these swine!" he harked into my ear. "That's who we beat our brains out to amuse! Do they appreciate what I've gone through, the aggravation, the sleepless nights I've spent over that show? Give 'em bread and circuses, hey? If I had my way, I'd give 'em something else!"

Heads turned the length of the car, and over the din I detected a subdued muttering like the sans-culottes in a Metro costume film. But Kerr, caught up in a crusading mood in which he identified himself with the Scarlet Pimpernel, was not to be diverted. He launched into a tirade on unions and the New Deal, concluding with a few generalizations that would have abashed even a Republican steering committee. I still marvel that we emerged intact from the Hudson Tubes. Up to the moment we did, I fully expected to expire in a blitzkrieg of lunch-pails.

Thanks to the headwaiter of the Biltmore, a paragon who refused to be intimidated by Kerr's hiccups and our crapulous exteriors, I got some breakfast into my charge, and at eight o'clock, Murray Zweifel appeared. His arrival was the signal for repeated fireworks. We were bracketed with Benedict Arnold and consigned to the devil, roundly notified by Kerr that hell would freeze over before he accompanied us to Boston. We argued and pleaded; at one point, under pretense of visiting the lav, Kerr slipped into a phone booth and was confiding all to Winchell when we extricated him by main force. In the quarter hour before train-time, the fracas degenerated into delirium. Just as the gates were closing, Murray and I bucked our way across Grand Central through a sea of astonished commuters, using Kerr as a battering ram. He was yelling vilification at us, a cataclysmic headache throbbed in my skull, and my reason hung by a thread, but nothing else mattered—the production was saved. From now on, I could relax, for the pathway ahead was strewn with roses. I was fated to learn something about botany, to say nothing of show business.

In the entertainment game, as Sir Arthur Wing Pinero was wont to observe in far loftier language, it don't pay to count your turkeys. At the Hub City premiere of *Sherry Flip*, the traveler curtain failed to open in the conventional fashion. Instead, it billowed out and sank down over the orchestra pit, perceptibly muffling the overture. The musicians fiddled manfully underneath, but Herman Earl's score was too fragile and lilting to overcome the handicap. The comedy, contrariwise, was all too robust—so much so that the police stepped in next day and excised four sketches. The reviews were unanimous. The show, it was agreed, was lavish enough to preclude spending another nickel on it; it should be closed as it stood. And then, on the very threshold of disaster, Kerr decided to rally. He fired the director and restaged the show himself, cut salaries to the bone, and sent a case of cognac to every critic in New York. His acumen bore fruit; we ran five nights there, and those who saw it grow garrulous even today at the memory of *Sherry Flip*. The last time I saw Poultney Kerr, he was a television nabob and beyond mortal ken, but he could not conceal his nostalgia for Broadway. He told me he was mulling an idea for a revue—a smart, intimate romp on the order of *The Garrick Gaieties*.

Front and Center, Kiddies!

I know it sounds incredible, but up to yesterday there was not the slightest indication from the New England Council of Hotel and Resort Proprietors regarding its slogan for the summer. As June faded slowly into July, thoughtful people began biting their nails and wondering what was amiss. "What slogan will govern more than a few New England resort hotels this summer!" everybody kept asking himself fretfully, lying down in a hammock and shading his face with a white drill hat. Then, just as the tension had become well-nigh unbearable, the Council broke silence in an electrifying release to the Boston *Globe*:

"Keep the guests tired out and happy" is the slogan that will govern more than a few New England resort hotels this summer, according to a survey recently completed by the New England Council....One particularly inspired New Hampshire hotel man outlined his plan for the current season so well that his program will be adopted by many another hotel in New England this summer.

"There'll be no rocking chair brigade here, if we can prevent it," he said.... "This year everyone in our establishment will double in brass. We're eliminating the doorman and stationing a bellhop outside. He'll also deliver cars (if any) to our garage. Everybody, including the manager, doubles in something. All help will be well paid and well fed. Two or three times during the season, we plan to give the employees a dinner and have the guests wait on them... Our main job is to keep everything moving at such a fast pace the guests will forget to complain about anything," he said.

For the benefit of any shut-in forced to forego his annual visit to Franconia, Truro, or Bar Harbor by his bank balance, I submit a reasonable facsimile of what he might have encountered. To properly establish the mood, one should rub the ankles lightly with poison ivy and swallow a bad clam.

(Scene: The porch of Eagle's Mere, at Durfee's Notch in the Berkshires. As the curtain rises, Pudovkin, the manager, is discovered lounging on the steps. He wears a bellhop's jacket much too small for him and chews on a half-dead cigar. The Bessemers, a stout, middle-aged couple, totter slowly up the driveway, laden with baggage. They collapse on the gravel, their faces streaming.)

PUDOVKIN: Kind of pooped, eh? You'll lose that bay window before we're through with you.

BESSEMER (*panting*): Say, bud, bring me a glass of water, will you?

MRS. BESSEMER: I'll take some plain ginger ale.

PUDOVKIN: Wouldn't you rather have a tall, cool rum collins with mint and lots of ice?

MRS. BESSEMER: Why, that sounds delicious.

PUDOVKIN (*comfortably*): Doesn't it? I'll hop down the mountain and get one. It's only four miles—the exercise'll do me good.

BESSEMER: Look, if it's any trouble, I'd just as soon—

PUDOVKIN: Nonsense, that's what I'm paid for, to run down every time some lush wants a snort. Or if you prefer, I can carry you down on my back.

MRS. BESSEMER (*nervously*): Maybe we ought to register first, Roy. Is the manager around?

PUDOVKIN: You're looking at him.

BESSEMER: That's right—of *course*! You've heard me speak of Mr. Pudovkin, lovekin—I mean, love.

MRS. BESSEMER: Many times.

BESSEMER: Well, this is Mr. Pudovkin. (*A pause*) You remember me—Roy Bessemer? I've been coming here for years.

PUDOVKIN (*shortly*): I've seen the face. It isn't the kind you recall.

MRS. BESSEMER: We'll just slip up to the room, if it's ready.

PUDOVKIN: It will be, when you change the linen. Did you bring a broom?

BESSEMER: Yes, right here in the golf bag. Rhoda's got the oil mop and the Dutch Cleanser in her suitcase.

PUDOVKIN: Wait a minute, you. What's that niblick doing there?

BESSEMER (*guiltily*): Er—I—I figured I'd play a few holes—you know, after my chores were done and like that—

PUDOVKIN (*savagely*): And get out of mowing the lawn, eh, you little sneak? I've got half a mind to bundle you back to town. If I didn't need waiters for the employees' banquet tonight—

S J Perelman

BESSEMER: Honest, Mr. Pudovkin, I don't have to use the greens. I'll practice in my room; it's more fun anyway.

PUDOVKIN: Well, we'll let it ride this once, but watch your step, Bosco. All right, go up and dress; you'll never get those napkins folded.

MRS. BESSEMER: Hurry, Roy, we'll have time for a quick bath.

PUDOVKIN: You don't think we turn the water on just for guests, do you?

MRS. BESSEMER: I'm not particular. An old rain barrel's plenty good enough for me.

PUDOVKIN: I know your kind. First it's a bit of soap, then ice water, and the next thing I know, you want the same food as the help. Now beat it. I don't like a lot of riffraff lousing up the front of the house.

BESSEMER: Yes, sir. Did you wish to see our references, Mr. Pudovkin?

PUDOVKIN (*wearily*): No, they're probably forged anyway.

(As the Bessemers exit, the curtain is lowered to denote the lapse of an hour. It rises on the dining room. Pudovkin, Nick, the busboy, and Hedwig, the maid, are seated amid rows of empty tables receding into the gloom. They wear paper hats marked "Savannah Line" and languidly sip their consommé, Pudovkin without removing his cigar. The Bessemers, in decent black, fuss over the second course at the sideboard.)

PUDOVKIN (*cackling*): Wait, you haven't heard the payoff. So we break down the door, and there's Mrs. Poultney in the Senator's pajamas!

NICK: Ha, ha, that's a pip! (*snapping his fingers at*

242

Bessemer) Hey, droopy, you forgot the butter chips.

BESSEMER: Coming right up, Mr. Eumenides.

HEDWIG (*indignantly*): Say, is this supposed to be chicken consommé?

PUDOVKIN: Boy, what a swindle. Waitress!

MRS. BESSEMER: Yes, sir?

PUDOVKIN: If this is chicken consommé, so is Lake Louise. And you can tell the manager I said so.

MRS. BESSEMER: But you're the manager, Mr. Pudovkin.

PUDOVKIN (*to the others*): Well, I've heard all the excuses, but that's a new one.

NICK (*pinching Mrs. Bessemer*): Hello, sweetie pie, how's about a little loving?

MRS. BESSEMER (*giggling*): Now you stop. I've got my work to do.

NICK: She's a red-hot mamma. I'll date her up yet.

HEDWIG (*taking out some crocheting*): Skirt-crazy, if you ask me. A regular wolf.

PUDOVKIN: Hell, you're only young once. What are you making, Miss Swenson?

HEDWIG: It's an all-purpose accessory. This way it's a purse, but when you put it on your head, it becomes a beanie.

PUDOVKIN: Very flattering. Listen, that reminds me. (*lowering his voice*) How much do you give these people?

HEDWIG: I generally leave a dime. That's all the service is worth.

NICK: Or the grub either. Jeez, it's brutal. We should have gone to Siegel's Mere.

PUDOVKIN: Up there you get free samba lessons by

the pool.

NICK (*voluptuously*): You said it. Beautiful, shapely maidens with nothing on.

HEDWIG: Don't you ever think of anything but sex?

NICK: No, it's kind of a hobby with me. Like woodworking.

BESSEMER: Are you ready for the roast, folks?

NICK: What is it—lamb?

PUDOVKIN: It's always lamb. (*He starts uncontrollably as he sees his portion.*)

BESSEMER (*anxiously*): Anything wrong, sir?

PUDOVKIN: Somebody swiped one of the nubbins. (*slowly*) And I've got a *pretty...good...*notion who it was. (*He collars Bessemer, plucks from his pocket a napkin containing the missing morsel.*)

BESSEMER (*falling to his knees*): It was midsummer madness, Mr. Pudovkin. Don't turn me in!

PUDOVKIN: There's an ugly name for that sort of thing, Bessemer.

BESSEMER: I know—nubbin swiping. (*Moaning*) The shock will kill my mother.

MRS. BESSEMER: Oh, Roy, for shame! The first night, too—before I even had a chance to steal a towel.

Pudovkin (*relenting*): Well, you've had your lesson. The Cannonball passes the junction in twenty minutes. If you're smart, you'll be on it.

MRS. BESSEMER (*fervently*): I'll never forget you, Mr. Pudovkin. I'll save my money and repay—

PUDOVKIN : No. Turn down my bed before you go. (*They slink out*)

HEDWIG (*softly*): You're a very gallant gentleman. Mihail Mihailovitch.

PUDOVKIN: No—just a sentimental Slav. (*He clears his throat roughly and lights a fresh cigar.*)

CURTAIN

Revulsion in the Desert

The doors of the D train slid shut, and as I dropped
into a seat and, exhaling, looked up across the aisle, the
whole aviary in my head burst into song. She was a
living doll and no mistake—the blue-black bang, the
wide cheekbones, olive-flushed, that betrayed the
Cherokee strain in her Midwestern lineage, and the
mouth whose only fault, in the novelist's carping
phrase, was that the lower lip was a trifle too voluptuous. From what I was able to gauge in a swift, greedy
glance, the figure inside the coral-colored bouclé dress
was stupefying. All the accessories, obviously, had come
from Hermès or Gucci, and you knew that some latter-
day Cellini, some wizard of the pliers like Mario
Buccellati, must have fashioned the gold accents at her
throat and wrists. She was absorbed in a paperback, the
nature of which I guessed instinctively; it was either
Rilke or Baudelaire, or even, to judge by the withdrawn
and meditative expression on her lovely face, Pascal.
Suddenly a pair of lynx eyes, gray and exquisitely
slanting, lifted from the page and fixed on me a long,
intent scrutiny that set my knees trembling like jellied
consommé. Could she have divined my adoration in her

246

telepathic feminine way? Ought I spring forward, commandeer the book, and read out to her the one passage that would make us kinsprits forever? Before I could act, the issue had decided itself. The train ground to a stop at the Thirty-fourth Street station, and as she arose and stowed the book in her handbag, I saw that it was Ovid's *Art of Love*.

A lump of anguish welled up in my throat at the opportunity I had let slip, the encounter that might have altered my whole destiny; I sought surcease in the advertising placards overhead, but they were as bitter aloes. How could a craven like me dare aspire to Miss Subways, whose measurements were 37-24-33, whose hair was auburn, and who was an enthusiastic kegler? Vic Tanny, urging me to discard adipose tissue at his health club, was at best a cruel reminder that I was no longer the arrowy Don Juan I supposed, and Breakstone's injunction to diet on its cottage cheese merely compounded the affront. I was preparing to debark at Forty-second Street, lacerated by self-pity, when I beheld a poster that mercifully set me off on quite another tangent. "Win a fantabulous week for two at the Cloudburst in Las Vegas plus $3500 in cash!" it trumpeted. "Play Falcon Pencil Company's Super-Duper Guessing Game!" I never ascertained whether I was to watch for some magic serial number or to hawk the pencils from door to door. In the next breath, I was ejected to the platform, and there superimposed itself on my mind a memory of this selfsame Cloudburst, fantabulous indeed, as I saw it during a brief enforced visit to Las Vegas just a year ago.

My trip to the gambling mecca was no casual

stopover between planes; I flew there from Rome, a matter of seven thousand-odd miles, to honeyfogle an actor, and I undertook the journey with the direst misgivings. The circumstances were somewhat as follows. Several months before, an Italian film producer had engaged me to devise a vehicle for a meteoric American tenor, whom it might be prudent to call Larry Fauntleroy. The latter, through his records and personal appearances, had scored a phenomenal success in the United States and Europe; his presence in a picture, it was universally felt, would make it a bonanza; and Signor Bombasti, from the moment I began work in Rome, announced himself ready to go to any lengths to win Fauntleroy's approval of our story. I soon found out what he meant. Shortly after completing the treatment, which is to say the narrative outline of the scenario, I was summoned to my employer, hailed as a composite of Congreve, Pirandello, and Norman Krasna, and urged to convey the manuscript in person to Fauntleroy. Nobody else, affirmed Bombasti, could adequately interpret its gusto and sparkle, its rippling mirth and delicious nuances. (And nobody else in the organization, he might well have added, spoke even rudimentary English.) My expostulations, my protests that I was anathema to performers, went for naught; in a supplication that would have reduced even Louis B. Mayer to tears, Bombasti entreated me, for the sake of the team, if not my own future, to comply. Seven hours later, I weighed in at Ciampino West airdrome.

The Milky Way, the hotel where I was scheduled to stay in Las Vegas and whose floor show Fauntleroy was currently headlining, was the town's newest—a vast, foolish beehive of plate glass rearing fifteen stories above the sagebrush, so ruthlessly air-conditioned that I was wheezing like an accordion by the time I unpacked. My quarters could only be described as a harlot's dream. The dominant colors of the sleeping chamber, a thirty-five-foot-long parallelogram, were jonquil and azure. A bed large enough to accommodate a *ménage à trois*, flanked by modernique gooseneck lamps with purple shades, occupied one wall; along the other, three abstract chairs in yellow plastic confronted a lacquer-red television set. To facilitate any makeup I might require, there was a theatrical vanity bordered with hundred-watt bulbs in the adjacent dressing room. Beyond it lay a ghastly black-tiled bathroom from which one momentarily expected Lionel Atwill to emerge in the guise of a mad surgeon, flourishing a cleaver.

Within a few minutes, my reason was sufficiently unsettled to regard the décor as normal, and, having erased the ravages of travel, I went in search of Fauntleroy. He was breakfasting at a table near the pool, encircled by the usual retinue of the popular entertainer—agents, managers, song pluggers, masseurs, and touts—all of them vying with each other to inflate his ego. I was introduced boisterously, if inaccurately, to the rest of the levée; Bombasti's cable heralding my arrival, it seemed, had miscarried, and for a while the troubadour was under the impression that I was a disc jockey from Cleveland. Rather than launch into tedious explanations, I accepted the role and ordered a steak and a cigar to render myself inconspicuous. Sprinkled around us on the greensward, half a hundred of the

Milky Way's guests dozed in the fierce sunlight, leaching away their cares to the strains of Nelson Riddle. When the voice of Frankie Stentorian started booming forth "Ciaou Ciaou Bambina," I chose the auspicious moment to properly identify myself as the emissary from Italy.

"Man, that story you wrote for me is a gasser!" Fauntleroy chortled, wringing my hand. "I haven't had a chance to read it yet, on account of I just opened here, but I'll get to it tonight between shows. Then you and I can spend the whole day tomorrow tearing it apart, analyzing and tightening so the plot practically writes itself. How does that suit you?"

I assured him I could hardly wait to eviscerate my handiwork, and, amid ecstatic predictions from his claque that the picture would outgross *The King of Kings*, withdrew. Inside the Milky Way casino, though it was only noon, several dozen patrons were already gathered at the faro and crap tables. They all moved with the languor of somnambulists—woebegone creatures condemned to spend eternity hopelessly defying the laws of chance. I watched a couple of blue-haired clubwomen pump silver dollars into the slot machines until their *cafard* communicated itself to me, and then progressed into a coffee shop that might have been lifted, along with its clientele, from a Southern bus terminal. Just as I was struggling to master a sandwich composed largely of lettuce and toothpicks, a music arranger out of my Hollywood past, named Dave Jessup, accosted me. Our salutations could not have been more joyful had we met on a sheep station in Queensland.

"Listen," said Jessup, after we had exhumed the age of fable and interred it again. "Everybody here flips about this new spectacle at the Cloudburst—the French revue called 'Oo La La !' What say we catch it tonight?"

To be candid, I was planning to retire early with the copy of Ruskin's *Stones of Venice* I had begun on the plane, as I wanted to see how it came out, but, sensing Jessup's desperate need of companionship, I good-naturedly yielded. Shortly before six, the fashionable dinner hour in Las Vegas, a cab deposited the pair of us under the neon volcano that skyrocketed from the block-long façade of the Cloudburst. In a ballroom the size of the Cirque Médrano, five hundred hysteroids in play togs were gorging themselves to a medley of jump tunes, magnified tenfold by microphones, issuing from a boxful of musicians on one wall. The din was catastrophic; we were shoved pell-mell into a booth, barricaded behind a cheval-de-frise of celery, and supplied with vases of whiskey that drenched our shirt fronts. A distracted waiter, hovering on the verge of collapse, unhesitatingly recommended snails as our main course, only to reappear in the blink of an eye with two filets that drooped over the sides of the plate. What with the uproar and the kaleidoscope flickering upon us, it was not easy to find my dish in the murk, and but for a sudden agonizing stab as Jessup tried to sever my knuckles, I never would have known I had eaten half his steak. Then our dinner vanished altogether, and as the orchestra sounded a fanfare, a deafening Gallic voice ushered in the pageant.

Whoever the creators of "Oo La La !" were, they were admirers of the undraped female form, for after establishing the locale as Montmartre with an apache dance and a chorus of gendarmes, they got down to brass tacks. A procession of sinuous long-stemmed beauties wound its way to the footlights attired in peasant costumes, large sections of which evidently had been lost in shipment from France. The mishap seemed to occasion the ladies small concern, however; they bore themselves proudly and endured the gaze of the audience without flinching. Their fortitude was rewarded by hearty applause intermingled with whistles, and as the last of them undulated offstage the scene inexplicably shifted to Naples. A *festa* was in progress, and a number of masked revelers of all sexes were holding carnival, dancing the tarantella and beating tambourines fit to wake the dead. Suddenly the clamor subsided, and another procession of coryphees, whose clothes had arrived piecemeal from Italy, wove downstage. They exhibited as much aplomb in the face of adversity as their French cousins had, and the audience paid them equal tribute. In both Turkey and Polynesia, to which we were then whisked in quick succession, the same regrettable shortages prevailed, but the houris and wahines were similarly undaunted. Having demonstrated to everyone's satisfaction that human nature under duress is constant the world over, the production soared to a climax. Four embossed trapdoors in the ceiling, hitherto masquerading as ventilators, vibrated shakily downward in time to the "Skaters' Waltz," disclosing a quartet of robust and untrammeled vestals clad in wisps of stockinet. They were lit from below, an angle calculated to maximize their charms, and the effect was hauntingly reminiscent of that greatest of all equine masterpieces Rosa Bonheur's "The Horse Fair."

I had become so preoccupied with the entertainment that I was ready to watch it a second, or even a third, time to familiarize myself with its catchy tunes and stage business, but Jessup demurred. He had arranged with two shapely girl violinists at the Golden Drugget, which from his description appeared to be a branch of the Juilliard School, to help them with their solfeggio, and invited me to accompany him. Mindful of the commitment I had made to disembowel my script the next day, however, I begged off and turned in at eight-thirty. About four, a phone call from Fauntleroy aroused me. He apologized for the intrusion, but he was terribly upset by the few pages of the treatment he had read. The background, the characters, the entire orientation were wrong. Nevertheless, he added quickly, I was not to agitate myself; I must get a good sound sleep, and in due course he would assess all the shortcomings. I rolled over and slept like a log.

It was midafternoon before I finally managed to awaken Fauntleroy, and another hour before he tottered into the coffee shop, unshaven and numb with seconal. When dexamyl had loosened his tongue, his whole mood changed. All the apprehensions he had voiced earlier on the phone, he told me, were groundless. Somewhere between sleep and waking he had evolved an idea for a series of production numbers that would make ours the most talked-of film of the century. "This is a whole fresh approach to the story, mind you," he began. "So for crisake be flexible in your thinking. Instead of a happy-go-lucky archeologist, the way you wrote me, I figure I'm a happy-go-lucky talent scout or an agent—sort of a singing Irving Lazar. I'm always going around to various exotic places, like France, Naples, Turkey, and Tahiti, rounding up these gorgeous contest winners for a floor show at the Copa or the Rainbow Room. So far so good. Now, here comes your drama. These girls arrive in plenty of time for the opening, all right, but the different parts of their native wardrobes are always confiscated at the last minute by the customs or lost in a typhoon or something. Do you get it? It's a race against overwhelming odds—a suspenseful strip tease that grows out of a real human situation...."

Seventy-two hours afterward, in the Eternal City, Signor Bombasti beamed at me across the managerial mahogany and rubbed his hands in satisfaction. Not only was I the wiliest diplomat since Prince Metternich, he declared, but, as Fauntleroy's cable in front of him attested, I was a grand human being. "And let us remember something else in our hour of triumph, my dear fellow," he reminded me. "It was I, Ettore Bombasti, who had the vision and the genius to marry your two outstanding talents."

"I'll remember it till the day I die," I said fervently. "I thought of it every minute I was in Las Vegas."

"Good," he said. "So long as you and our Larry saw eye to eye, so long as there was a meeting of minds, I ask for nothing more. This will be the biggest box-office attraction since *The King of Kings*. Now go back to your study and write as you have never written before."

I did. In fact, I wrote as *nobody* had ever written before.

I Declare, Under Penalty of Milkshake

I was drifting around the periphery of the Village the other morning, luxuriating in the sunshine and mingling freely with the indigenes—the Method actors with stormy faces and fat ankles, the models as angular as the Afghans who drew them along, the leather craftsmen nursing dreams of sandals too abstract to contemplate—when a placard in a drugstore suddenly beckoned. The window was one whose anatomical displays had long endeared it to me; many's the time I had browsed over its variegated charts of the human interior, full of conduits and stairways, in which Lilliputians played badminton in the cranium and stoked furnaces in the belly to demonstrate the efficacy of some gland preparation. Latterly, the principal exhibit had been a full-size wax replica of a man's head, the left side of it bald as Henri Landru's and the right sprouting wiry black bristles. This miraculous rebirth, the work of a tonic displayed nearby, appeared to have unhinged the user to a degree, for his eyeballs were rolling wildly and his tongue protruded in anguish. Whether conducive to hair or dementia, however, the lotion was now nowhere in evidence. Instead, the forefront of the window was occupied by a boldly lettered sign reading, "Income Tax Returns Prepared Here by Expert."

Ordinarily, I leave such grubby matters to a worthy whom I'd pit against any comprador in Hong Kong, but, as it happened, he was cruising in the Norfolk Broads—or so I had interpreted his last message—and the chance to dispense with his services excited my cupidity. Why not avail myself of this windfall and save a considerable fee? After all, there was nothing so recondite about executing a tax form; I had read a goodish bit of Sylvia Porter and J. K. Lasser in my day, and without vainglory felt I had an instinctive flair for elucidating the mumbo-jumbo of revenue. I pushed open the door and strode in forcefully. At once I went into a Chaplinesque stagger to circumvent half a dozen tables, littered with breakfast debris, that consumed most of the floor space. At the fountain, and plainly impervious to the clutter, a swarthy attendant in a green surgical smock was draped over a scratch sheet. I squirmed through the forest of libidinous paperbacks obscuring the rear of the store and sought out the prescription desk. It was so burdened with toiletries, greeting cards, candy, analgesics, and assorted medical lumber that it took some reconnaissance to find the druggist, who, it developed, was merely a pharmacy major spelling the proprietor.

"I don't handle the tax work," the youth told me feverishly. "I'm busy on a rush order—digitalis for a heart case. Talk to the guy over there."

"The soda clerk?" I asked, taken aback. "Does he make up the declarations?"

"I think so," he said, "but I'm new here. I took over while my uncle's away. He went to Peru for some ipecac."

He flew back to his pestle, and as I stood irresolute, the party behind the fountain hailed me. "What type return you want to file, bud?" he called out genially. "Individual or corporation ?"

"Well, I haven't quite made up my mind," I began, chilled by a premonition of disaster. "I was just scouting around—"

"Probably the head of a household—right?" he said encouragingly. "Okey-doke. Sit down by the table and I'll bring a 1040 blank." Before I could collect my faculties, he had circled the counter, cutting off the only avenue of retreat, and plumped himself down. "Now, give me the whole picture, remember," he warned, spreading out his documents fanwise. "No chiseling—you dig! We don't want to do anything that smacks of fraud."

"Good gracious, no," I protested in a high, girlish voice that seemed altogether alien. For some inexplicable reason, there arose before me an image of the two of us in a railroad coach, manacled to a federal marshal. The muscles in my calves started to flutter.

"After all," he pursued, "why should I perjure myself for some measle who gives me a lousy three bucks to fill out his form?"

"You'd be a fool," I agreed.

"In spades," he said. "All right, let's get going. To the best of your knowledge and belief, is everything you are about to disclose a true, correct, and complete statement?"

"Well—er—truth's pretty much of an abstraction,

isn't it?" I asked, suddenly conscious of how warm it was in the store. "I mean, the ancients held, philo-sophically speaking—"

"Look, save that schmalz for the review agent later on," he interrupted. "I'm just trying to extract the info they want on this blank. During the taxable year, did you derive any income out of dividends, interest, rents, pensions, and like that?"

I shook my head.

"How about wages, salaries, bonuses, commissions, tips, or other compensation?"

"I think so," I replied, after a moment's reflection, "but I haven't any figures on me. I'd have to look in my checkbook at home."

"Ach, nobody's twisting your arm for the exact amount," he said carelessly. "The main thing is, was it under or over a hundred dollars? That is, after payroll deductions."

"Let me see," I pondered. "Do you want the gross or the net?"

"I don't understand what those words mean," he said, with an irritable gesture. "You made a hundred dollars more or less—that's close enough. Now, then, what source did you get this income from?"

"Well, a movie outfit in Europe, mainly," I said. "I did a picture for this Italian studio in Rome last summer."

My counselor beamed and smote the table resound-ingly." How do you like that!" he exclaimed. "The minute you came in, I spotted you for an actor. There was something flashy about you."

"I—er—I'm not actually a performer," I pointed out. "I wrote the screenplay, as they call it." He blinked at me. "You know, the plot and the lines the different characters say."

"What are you trying to do, con me?" he demanded, with manifest cynicism. "The actors make up all that junk as they go along."

"Yes, but somebody has to take the blame for it in case of a lawsuit," I explained.

"Like a scapegoat, you mean," he said thoughtfully. "Say, that wouldn't be a bad racket to break into. Do they really pay off for that kind of a rap?"

"Well, it brings me in walking-around money," I admitted. "But listen, getting back to my return—"

"Excuse me a minute while I wait on these heads," he broke in, jumping to his feet. Two young ladies, in toreador pants and mohair sweaters, whose swirling coiffures looked as though they had been squeezed from an icing gun, had ranged themselves at the fountain. They studied the menu posted over the coffee urn with languid contempt.

"Tuna-fish and cream-cheese sandwiches," one of them sighed, wrinkling her nose in distaste. "Holy cat, Dominic, don't you ever have any hot dishes?"

"You two are the hottest on the lower West Side," the soda clerk returned gallantly. "It's fracturing the fire laws just to let you in here. What'll it be, girls?"

After extended thought, the pair chose some dire amalgam of apple butter, sausage, and raisins called a Driftwood Special, and, plunging straws into their malteds, lapsed into an intent discussion of hair lacquer. I studied the section of the document before me pertaining to medical and dental deductions, but soon floundered into a bog of technicalities about the excess of Line 3 over Line 4 that brought back all my youthful reading reversals. Just as I was mulling the advisability of paying Dominic his three-dollar ransom and decamping, he rejoined me, energetically rubbing his hands.

"Now, one or two questions and you're all through," he said, with the brisk benevolence of a doctor in a TV commercial. "First, we fill in this space here." He laboriously printed the word "scapegoat" in the block designating my occupation, and then, turning to the instructions overleaf, scanned them narrowly. "In connection with that job in Italy, you had certain travel expenses, like transportation and hotels, did you not?"

"Reimbursed," I said.

"Sure, but you must have laid out dough for *something*," he insisted. "What about starlets from the production that you had to take out and coach them in their roles?"

"There was—ahem—a minimum of coaching," I said. "My wife accompanied me on the trip."

"Listen, Clyde, get the rocks out of your head," he sighed. "You need that moo more than the government. Try and think."

"Well…" I hesitated. "Come to think of it, I did ship my dog overseas in the middle of the summer."

"There you are!" said Dominic, his face lighting up. "In your view, was the animal necessary to your peace of mind while you were working?"

"*Necessary?*" I repeated. "They gave him equal billing with me on the screen credits—that's how necessary he was."

"Then it's deductible—every Goddam cent," he

replied firmly, "and we'll carry it right up to the Supreme Court if we have to. How much did it cost to send over your pet?"

"Hmm, let's see," I ruminated. "A hundred and thirty-eight dollars for plane fare, nine for the cab to Idlewild, and eighteen for the crate they made me buy there. Then he broke out of the box in Amsterdam while they were transshipping him—"

"And you had to hire a lawyer to trace him," Dominic prompted.

"I did?" I asked in surprise. "What sort of a lawyer?"

"Why, a Dutch one," he said blandly. "The most expensive kind in the world. Yes siree, I figure we can knock off about seven hundred bucks on that item alone."

"It seems a trifle high," I said. "Do you think we can make it stick?"

He shrugged impatiently. "All *right*, so they'll disallow half," he said. "My motto is give a little, take a little—we don't want to be a hog. Now, there's still one more point to cover—Line 9 here. Did you make any profit or loss from farming in the taxable year?"

"Well—ah—a little of each," I said cautiously. "We had a nice stand of grain down at my place in Pennsylvania. I don't remember what they call it—it's something like Wheatena, only more crunchy."

"How much did the seeds cost?" Dominic inquired. "If it's more than you got for the crop, then you finished in the red. You see why, don't you?"

"Not exactly," I said. "To be frank, I concentrate mostly on our other crops, such as honeysuckle and woodbine. My work's largely managerial—you know,

261

watching them through the windows, seeing that the different roots are in place, that sort of thing."

"Good," he approved. "Then you're entitled to charge for your services at, say, fifty bucks a week against any profit you made from the Wheatena, which means you write off another twenty-six hundred smackers." He made a rapid calculation and emitted a whistle. "Man !" he said. "With those expenses and your wife's exemption, you're going to get a hell of a rebate from the Treasury Department."

"I'm certainly glad I saw your sign in the window," I said, reaching for my billfold. "Is there a notary public around who could witness my signature?"

"Yep, at the delicatessen in the next block," he replied. He stowed the fee in his smock and shook my hand warmly. "Much obliged, Jack, and good luck. Say, I forgot to ask—what's that picture you did in Italy about?"

"A kraut named Baron Munchausen," I said. "An eccentric who used to make up fibs."

"Not for Baby," said Dominic emphatically. "I get enough screwballs here in the daytime. When I go to the movies, I want to see a story based on real life."

As if on cue, the door shot open to admit a paper-thin individual no taller than a Watusi and no more bizarre, except that his face was a distinct turquoise blue. He hurried to the fountain and, mounting a stool, began to drum a nervous tattoo on the Bromo–Seltzer tap. With a wink in my direction that rattled the fixtures, Dominic departed to serve him.

A few seconds later, loungers in the vicinity of Sheridan Square might have observed another individual, paper-fat and ashen-faced, emerge from a local drugstore. He deposited the paper in an adjacent trash can, entered a coin booth, and dialed the long-distance operator. "I want to speak to this tax consultant in Norfolk, Virginia, Miss," he said urgently, "but I don't know precisely where. I think he's cruising with some broads."

Three Loves Had I, in Assorted Flavors

There it lay in a dusty recess of our Pennsylvania attic, atop a pile of other discarded records—Cole Porter's "Experiment," played by Ray Noble and his orchestra —and there I crouched that winter's day, heart-stricken, simianlike, to avoid concussing myself against the rafters. To think that a quarter of a century had elapsed since I used to play it over and over, marveling at the smooth precision of the brass, the buoyant lines in the refrain so characteristic of Porter: "The apple on the top of the tree/ Is never too high to achieve./ So take an example from Eve./Experiment!" Heavy with nostalgia, I bore it downstairs, and when our laundryman peered through the window ten minutes later, he saw his customer, eyeballs capsized, gliding about with a broom in his arms, an unreasonable facsimile of Fred Astaire. Why I was thus engaged, or what associations the song held for me, I could never explain to such a hayseed, but I can do so here. "Experiment" was the outstanding tune in *Nymph Errant*, an English musical I labored to convert into a Hollywood film back in the thirties, and now that TV's jackals roam where once I fought and bled, the sorry

264

tale may finally be told.

The architect of my misfortunes was, in actuality, a very decent bird—a producer named Sonny LoPresto, who himself was a successful songwriter and Broadway celebrity. From the outset his attitude was refreshingly candid and succinct; he made no effort to minimize the problems ahead. "Kid, I'll be honest with you," he said through his knees. (The armchairs in his office were so deep that we could hardly discern each other's face.) "This property was wished on me by Wingfoot Shaughnessy, the head of the studio. He saw it in London, with Gertie Lawrence in the lead, and he flipped—bought it on the spot. Now, it's a great Cole Porter score, a crackerjack, but the book— Well, it's going to need lots of elbow grease to get a picture out of it. Which is why I'm teaming you with Cy Horniman on the screenplay."

"Cy Horniman?" I repeated incredulously. "But his specialty is hoods. He wrote all that underworld stuff for Cagney over at Warner's."

"Damn right he did," said LoPresto, beaming. "He's got a terrific plot sense—he'll give you enough sit-uations to make a hundred musicals. So what if the guy only thinks in terms of blood and guts? Use him—milk his brain!"

It baffled me that, of the twelve hundred and fifty members of the Screen Writers' Guild, LoPresto couldn't have picked a pen with a daintier nib to comple-ment mine. However, professional ethics enjoined silence, and I acquiesced—not without foreboding.

Horniman was hours late for our initial conference the next morning, and when he did totter in, unshaven and half asleep, he looked pretty shopworn. His face, which bore remnants of the starry-eyed beauty typified by Nell Brinkley's Adonises in the Hearst press, was puffy with dissipation, and a resentful scowl, as of one persecuted beyond endurance, corroded his forehead. As he fell back on the davenport in my office, racked by yawns, I noticed he was wearing a suede tie spattered with food stains. It was an unimportant detail, but I had a premonition our union was going to be shortlived.

"Christ, what a hangover," he murmured, combing his hair with his fingers. "We must have killed two quarts of tequila last night in Olvera Street, this Mexican cooz and I. My head is so hot you could fry an egg on it." He paused—I suspected, waiting for me to produce a skillet—but I registered polite concern and said nothing. "Well, anyhow," he resumed, "I wish I'd met Conchita ten years ago. I wouldn't be paying alimony to those two vampire bats I married. They stripped me of everything but what I've got on."

I could understand why they had left him his tie; nevertheless, I pretended commiseration, and delicately inched around to our project. Horniman confessed he had not yet read the basic material, but he said he would digest it that evening.

Two days passed by without any word, during which I built up a substantial head of steam. On the third he phoned to propose that we work at his home to escape the distractions of the studio. His lair, when I ultimately found it, thirteen miles below the Signal Hill oil fields, turned out to be a bungalow in a heavily wooded canyon —a refuge, he explained, from leeches like process servers and federal tax agents.

"Hell, it's too late in the day to talk script," he said, and cracked his knuckles. "I had Conchita prepare us lunch before she left for the cannery, so we'll just have a little snort and relax. Do you drink Moscow mules?"

I never had; nor, judging from the effects, will I ever be induced to again. After a purely nominal intake I experienced a feeling of exaltation, in the course of which I gobbled quantities of cold frijoles washed down with muscatel. There ensued a sudden thunderclap, as though I had been hit with a broadaxe, and then I was face down on the patio listening to my collaborator, garbed in a sarape and sombrero, pick out "Las Cuatro Milpas" on a guitar. The subject of *Nymph Errant* did not arise, needless to say, and our two subsequent meetings at the studio were similarly fruitless. Horniman was in a strange comatose state on both occasions; his conversation rambled, and I detected a sickly-sweet odor, unfamiliar to me at that time, emanating from his cigarettes.

A day or two afterward LoPresto summoned me to his office. "Don't bother to tell me how the yarn is going," he said. "I'll tell you. Your partner's on Cloud Nine and I've decided to replace him. From now on, you work with Byron Burrows, the author of *Dead on Arrival*."

"Sonny, this is a *musical*," I protested. "What kind of casting is that? Burrows is Horniman all over again—another gangland expert!"

"Yep, and a first-rate story mind," he said. "He's just the man to supply the skeleton for your brittle, sparkling japes. So get over there pronto and huddle with him—he's in that adobe villa across from Wardrobe."

Whereas most scenarists were housed in buildings like the Irving J. Thalberg Memorial, at Metro—whose façade doubled as an apartment dwelling or a high-grade mortuary on occasion—Burrows was permitted his own bower, and it was a lulu. To paraphrase Dashiell Hammett's dictum "The cheaper the crook the gaudier the patter," it was a case of the cheaper the scribe the gaudier the pad. The décor was a mixture of schools—the pecky-cypress walls adorned with pewter, fusing La Cienega Boulevard with Louisburg Square; an English kneehole desk; *toile-de-Jouy* curtains; and even a ceramic fox of the sort found in Madison Avenue antique shops. Burrows, a pallid, bespectacled chap, arose to greet me from a swollen red-leather lounge chair. In a community where facial tics were a commonplace, his were exceptional; they literally pursued each other across his features like snipe. The source of his turbulence soon became apparent—he was the most fearful hypochondriac I had ever met. We had barely started to discuss an approach to *Nymph Errant* when Burrows chanced to emit a slight cough. Instantly he was on his feet, groping toward a shelf crammed with medical books. He thumbed through one of them, hurriedly consulted an illustration, and collapsed into his chair.

"Finished," he croaked. "I've had it—I'm done for. Oh, my God."

I took the volume—Koch's standard work on tuberculosis—and looked at the plate, a detail drawing of lymph nodes in technicolor warranted to freeze the marrow. In my naïveté I sought to persuade the man that his alarm was unfounded, but he was impervious to reason. Throughout our association he was forever swallowing lozenges, spraying his throat, scanning his fingers for non-existent pustules, and palpating his abdomen, and much of the time he was so busy taking his temperature that he was speechless. Like all imaginary invalids, he felt he had evolved a regimen that catered to his special needs. At 11 A.M. our secretary brought him a tall glass of buttermilk and half a glass of bourbon. At four the dosage was reversed—a large bourbon followed by a small buttermilk. During our fortnight together there was no visible change in his condition, but we managed to eviscerate *Nymph Errant* and construct a species of framework. Though we had minor disagreements—like his insistence that Dion O'Banion and Bugs Moran would quicken the action— our relationship was amicable. One Monday, though, the secretary greeted me with chilling news. Burrows had suffered an attack of the rams over the Sabbath and had been removed to a rest home in Tucson to dehydrate.

"Buck up, my boy," Sonny LoPresto counseled as I sat in his quarters, profoundly discouraged. He quoted numberless ordeals. out of his Broadway past that had ended in triumph. "I know how rough it's been, but we're out of the woods at last. I've been combing the agents' lists and I've got you the perfect teammate— Lothar Perfidiasch, the noted Hungarian playright."

"And plagiarist," I supplemented. "He's been sued for every play and movie he ever wrote—or, rather, didn't."

"Granted, but a great constructionist," he emphasized. "After all, there's only six basic plots in the world, and it's up to you, with your shrewd nose for the unusual, to winnow out his ideas and select the least obvious. He's waiting for you in the commissary."

As indeed he was, over a third *Schlagobers*, his crafty eyes atwinkle above the white carnation he always sported; he was well aware of the disarming influence of flowers. The usual anecdotes about Ferenc Molnár and Budapest tricksters consumed our first afternoon. Subsequently Perfidiasch started bunting plots at me one after another, all too familiar to steal—*Fifty Million Frenchmen, Lady, Be Good, Roberta, A Connecticut Yankee*, along with everything Maugham and Sherwood and Coward had written. In the end I consented to one I couldn't identify—a farce of Georges Feydeau's, I discovered years later—and we fell to work.

Some seven weeks thence, just as we were nearing the final sequence of the screenplay, LoPresto called us in. He was pink with embarrassment. "Men, it kills me to break the news to you, but there's been a terrible mistake," he said. "Wingfoot Shaughnessy is convinced that the *Nymph Errant* he saw in London was about some dames who open a charm school for sourdoughs in the Klondike. Maybe it was, or maybe he ate too many liqueur candies that night. Anyway, he's the boss, and when I told him our version he blew his stack and canceled the picture. Turn in your kimonos."

I was eastward bound aboard the Chief the following noon, and it was many months before I heard the coda to our *Phantasiestück*. On the day I left, a young novelist, freshly arrived from New York to adapt his book, checked into the studio and was assigned my office. In rummaging through the desk, he came upon our script and, eager to absorb the technique of screenwriting, lay down on the davenport to peruse it. Uninured to the damp chill of southern California, he switched on the petcock of the gas radiator, nobody having warned him that it must be lit manually. He was slowly drifting toward the Final Fadeout when, by the happiest, of coincidences, salvation appeared in the form of my collaborator. Perfidiasch, in search of his cigar case, threw open the door and beheld the recumbent azure-faced stranger. His behavior, if indefensible by medical standards, at least saved the young man's bacon. He pummeled and shook him violently back to consciousness, and, before the other could rally his thoughts, began excoriating him. "What are you doing, you idiot?" he shouted. "Are you crazy? They find you here, a stiff with these dialogue pages on your chest, and the next thing you know, my friend is dragged off the train at Needles on a murder rap! ...*Say*—could this be an idea for a picture? Excuse me, I must call up Sol Wurtzel at Fox right away...."

Call Me Monty, and Grovel Freely

Baron Teviot of Burghclere, 33, who until his father's death Sunday was Charles John Kerr, plans to go back to work as a trainee supermarket checker. "We are the same people whether I have a title or not," he told reporters. "And the rent still has to be paid. I shall go on working for a living."....He wants customers to go on calling him Charlie.

                                                 —New York Post

All right, so Marcy and I were cornball, a couple of Americans on our first trip to England and doing the whole tourist bit. Windsor Castle, the Tower, Portobello Road, Hampton Court—you name it, we saw it. I said to Marcy when we got to London, "Look, angel," I said, "if there's one thing that bugs me it's somebody who's afraid to be mistaken for a square. I'm an ordinary person— maybe a little luckier than most. Just because I happen to be a big wheel back home, a junior assistant associate of a top news magazine, with my name on the masthead, I'm not going to throw my weight around. Our bureau chief here could show me a lot of inside stuff, but we'd never get the feel of the country—you follow? We're foreigners—let's behave like it." Which we did, and you never saw such red-carpet treatment. The British excel in Old World courtesy. You can't walk down a street without some bobby, twirling his nightstick, pointing out a quaint pub or a monument from the Wars of the Roses. The very stones under your feet seem to be saturated with tradition.

And the shopping! I don't know if anyone has commented on this before, but London is a man's town—I mean, it caters to the masculine sex. You wouldn't believe the wealth of hats and sweaters and shirts on view along Piccadilly and Bond Street; the two of us used to come back to the hotel every night dead tired, loaded with bundles. Marcy got some nice things, too—a cute leather address book to fit in her purse and a box of those chocolate-covered mints women love. I hadn't planned on buying any clothes except a tweed jacket or so and a few pairs of slacks, until Tom Greshler at the bureau talked me into having some suits made in Savile Row. Well, sir, it was one hell of an experience. His tailor's was like a cathedral, all walnut-paneled and Dickensian sporting prints, and three different cutters to measure the coat, weskit, and trousers. I got into a real bind with the man in charge of the coat, though. He kept nagging me to let them pad the shoulders and nip in the waist, and I finally had to straighten him out.

"Listen, what do you think I am—a gigolo?" I asked him. I wasn't aggressive—just firm. "Next thing I know, you'll have me wearing a monocle. I can't afford to look like a freak at the office, Algy—we're a conservative outfit. Either copy this Brooks model of mine or knock it off."

That did the trick, and from then on they were as

273

sweet as pie. They yessed me to death, arranged to mail over my duds without fittings and all that jazz, and never even asked for identification for my Express checks. Tom thought it'd be a good idea work-wise for me to see the inside of an English club while I was there, so he and I went around to the Cheesemongers, which extends guest privileges to our staff. One tradition of this male stronghold still observed from yesteryear, I learned, is a washroom where the brushes and combs are chained to the wall to prevent their being stolen. As luncheon fare, we partook of a cut off the joint, two vegs., and a pint of bitter, and after I lay down in the reading room for a spell I felt OK again. While drenched in the atmosphere, I dashed off a couple of notes to our researchers in New York, with gags like "Well, slaves, here I am in jolly old Lunnon," etc. Their eyes must have popped when they saw the club stationery.

The minute I got back to the hotel that afternoon Marcy was bursting with some kind of news. In that typical feminine way, it was upside down and backward, but I finally pieced it together. An hour before, in the tearoom at Harrods, she'd run into Ailsa and Jock Beasley, who belong to our country club in Smoke Hills.

"You remember Montague Pauncefoot, don't you?" Marcy reminded me. "The English checker at the Val-U-Mart—the thin blond boy?"

"Sort of a washed-out character, with a smirk?"

"Yes, but very nice," she said. "Well, he's suddenly become a nobleman—Lord Grubstone. The papers were full of it—how he was keeping the job in spite of his title and preferred to remain just plain Monty and heaven knows what. I guess it was so much talk, though, because hardly a week later, Ailsa heard, he and his wife returned to England."

"It figures," I said. "After all, a peer like that has responsibilities toward his tenants—the gamekeepers and farmers who till his estates....You know, now I think of it, there *was* something rather distinguished about him. His carriage, or maybe the bone structure in his face."

"That wasn't the impression you gave. You said he was an obnoxious little pimple."

"Will you kindly stop putting words in my mouth, for Chrisake?" I said. "Sure, he had a somewhat unusual accent, but they can't help that—it's part of their lineage. No, we were on damned good terms, Monty and I, and I often meant to ask him out to the house."

"Well, you missed the boat."

"Not at all," I said. "Why couldn't we look him up here? He's a democratic guy—he'd get a bang out of a couple of his old customers dropping by."

"Don't be absurd," she said. "I grant you he was always very generous with cartons, and helpful when I couldn't find the horseradish or whatever, but he'd never remember us, honest and truly. Now let's forget it—I have to change if we're to make the night tour of Soho."

Well, I saw there was no sense arguing, and clammed up. The next morning, though, I called Tom's secretary at the bureau and asked for a quick rundown on a certain titled family, the location of their ancestral seat, and the sightseeing in the vicinity. By the end of the day I had the info I needed and everything in readiness.

Marcy was pretty suspicious when I started bleating about this ruined abbey in Oxfordshire we mustn't miss; the old female intuition told her something was cooking, but I snowed her with a lot of doubletalk about Chaucer and Piers Plowman the secretary had pulled out, and she gave in. So right after breakfast we caught a train to a place with a name that broke us up— Leighton Buzzard—and taxied out to the ruins. It was nothing you'd look at twice, of course—half a dozen beat-up arches covered with ivy—and I didn't blame Marcy for crabbing at the trouble we'd gone to. I waited until we got back into the cab to spring it.

"Who owns most of the ground hereabouts?" I queried the driver. "Is it part of an estate or something?"

"Yes, Lord Grubstone's, sir. The Hall is up there, just beyond that copse."

"You're kidding!" I said. "Of all the fantastic— Marcy, did you hear that? Monty, the Val-U-Mart fellow—five minutes away! It's a perfect opportunity to buzz over and say hello—we'd be dopes not to!"

She knew it was a put-up job, but she couldn't squawk with the driver listening, and before she had a chance to we were on our way. The house, instead of the huge, frowning affair with turrets I expected, was on the dinky side, a grayish stone box the size of a branch library, squatting on a half acre of gravel. The butler who answered the door—and he took his time about it—looked like a road-company Robert Morley at the Paper Mill Playhouse. He gave us a frosty once-over, and when I said our name didn't matter, we wanted to surprise His Lordship, he motioned us into a side chamber. It seemed to be only a storeroom, judging from the case of stuffed birds and a set of *Punch* dating back to 1841, but all of a sudden a red-nosed old gaffer, in a stock, shot up from an armchair he was asleep in. The way he reacted, you'd have thought we came off a flying saucer.

"I say, what are you—Australians?" he exclaimed.

I told him, and that really alarmed him.

"Actually? I've never seen any before. Er—excuse me."

He scurried out, and as Marcy began needling me to leave, Monty appeared. For a split second I had trouble recognizing him. He wasn't wearing the white duster and the pencil behind his ear any longer, naturally; he had on like a Little Lord Fauntleroy costume—a velvet suit with a ruffled shirt foaming out of the collar—and he wore his hair in a tomboy bang. But also his whole manner was different—a mixture of peevish and hoity-toity, totally unlike the old days.

"Yes?" he snapped out. "You wished to see me?"

Figuring we might have interrupted him in a game of chess or something, I took the bull by the horns—recalled ourselves to him and congratulated him on his new status.

To my amazement he gave us a complete deadpan. "I'm afraid you're quite mistaken," he drawled, looking down his nose. "I *have* been in the States briefly, but never under the circumstances you describe. If I may say so, the American visitor to our shores sometimes tends to become a bit—ah—*dérangé*."

I started to get hot under the collar. "Are you suggesting we're unbalanced?" I said. "Why, Marcy and I have seen you at the check-out counter for the past—"

"Sweetheart, let's go," she interrupted. "Lord Grubstone's right—we've made a stupid error, apparently."

His face grew a little more human. "Frightfully sorry to cause you this misapprehension," he said. "You *are* guests in this country, I suppose....Look here—we were just sitting down to lunch with some people. Perhaps you'd care to join us?"

Well, Marcy wouldn't hear of it, but I was so mystified and at the same time riled by his reception that I insisted. Also, for one molding opinion on the foreign-news desk, it was a splendid chance to observe British aristocracy at close range. There were eight or nine persons, mainly oldsters, chattering away in the dining room, and hardly anyone looked up when our host introduced us as newcomers from overseas. I was wedged in next to a horsy old party with porcelain choppers who was lambasting Harold Wilson. Pretty soon he turned and, out of the blue, asked how long I'd been in the Coldstream Guards. I said I never was.

"But you must have done, damn it," he said. "You're wearing their regimental tie."

I explained I had bought it at Turncoat's, in Jermyn Street, the day before.

"Then take it back at once, man," he said, his wattles quivering like a turkey's. "You ought to be ashamed, parading around under false colors. No wonder the country's going to the demnition bowwows."

I was about to pin his ears back when a gargoyle in a beaded hat opposite quickly chimed in. The mischief had started in America, where nothing was sacred, she claimed. "And what do you expect, with that intolerable central heating of theirs? It dries up the mucous membrane, addles one's speech—"

"To say nothing of the swindling," another old buzzard croaked. "The worst bobbery I've met with this side of Shanghai. You put a sixpence in a stamp machine and the wretched thing invariably holds back a penny. The Mafia's share, of course."

That broke the ice, and they all began sounding off. A chap's shoes were likely to be stolen from outside his hotel room, and decent food was unobtainable; you couldn't buy a pilchard anywhere for love or money. I was so burned up by then, what with Grubstone's pretense of not being Monty and his sitting there, the muzzler, relishing us squirm, that I wanted to grab Marcy and blow the joint. Still, I felt I had to unmask the faker, make him admit we knew him when. And just like that, the inspiration came to me—*voom*.

I raised my voice a trifle—enough to carry to the head of the table. "Speaking of stamps, My Lord," I said blandly, "my wife over there and I have a beef that involves you. Why didn't you folks at the Val-U-Mart ever give out any green or blue ones, like the Acme or the Grand Union?" The entire place got deathly still— not a sound. "I'll tell you why," I said, gathering momentum. "Because you were a cheap, fly-by-night outfit, a bunch of chiselers. You handled the crummiest brand names, the most inferior meats, and baked goods you could insulate a roof with, and, brother, what a markup—ten and fifteen cents on each item!...No, Marcy, I won't shut up—he knows the score! He knows how they cheated us on the empty bottles we brought back, those flimsy bags that burst halfway to the car.

They taught him how to gouge the public, never you fear!"

Well, it was almost scary, the effect of my taunt. I had in mind to jolt the truth out of him, bring him down off his high horse, but I didn't dream the form it would take. His expression slowly changed like Jack Palance's in *Jekyll and Hyde*; one moment he was the smooth, disdainful dandy born to the purple, the next he was out of his chair, a raging fiend. He was practically incoherent. "That's a typical customer for you!" he shouted. "Yes, I know your kind, all right—clogging the express lane with twelve loaves of white bread, mixing up the dog food, mauling the bananas! You're the type that buys a pint of coleslaw after sampling the whole delicatessen case, that cadges free suet from the butcher to save on birdseed, that leaves his shopping cart in a snowdrift at the end of the parking area! Oh, I've seen you altering the prices on the canned salmon, filching beet greens to put in your soup!" He hammered on the tabletop with his clenched fists. "I hate every mother's son of you—do you hear? I rue the day I ever set foot in New Jersey!"

Whether it was the man's humiliation at being exposed in his own home or the strain of his outburst, that settled Lord Grubstone's hash; he was still sitting there, with egg on his face and the company frozen like the waxworks at Madame Tussaud's, as the two of us made our exit. Marcy didn't have much to say until the train had left Leighton Buzzard, and then she opened up. It was pretty personal stuff, but, to tell the truth, I wasn't listening. I was too busy formulating in my mind's eye the story I was going to cable back on swinging London and the decay of the British Establishment.

Be a Cat's-Paw! Lose Big Money!

Anybody can be a wiseacre after the fact, so let's get one thing straight at the outset. In chronicling the complications that arose from a note I found this spring in a bottle on Martha's Vineyard, I am not whining for sympathy or seeking to condone my behavior. If a totally unselfish gesture to a stranger—a benefaction, really—is wrong, then I was culpable and richly deserving of what I got. Impulsive, overly sentimental I may have been, but never throughout the ensuing imbroglio, I contend, was I prompted by base or ignoble motives. On the contrary, I like to think that, though an innocent dupe, I acquitted myself at all times with a dignity, a gentility, few other dupes in my position would have displayed. That is what I like to think.

The circumstances under which I discovered the note couldn't have been less dramatic. I was strolling along South Beach on the Vineyard one morning midway between Gay Head and Zack's Cliffs, and there, squarely in my path, lay a flask of the sort that usually contains stuffed olives. On the scrap of paper inside, in a clearly juvenile hand, was the following: "My name is Donald Cropsey. I am twelve years old. I

281

live at 1322 Catalpa Way, Reliance, Ohio. I have been visiting on Nantucket for a week. I threw this bottle off the ferryboat between Nantucket and Woods Hole, Mass., on Saturday. Please write me a note telling me when and where you found it."

Now, twelve-year-old boys, and especially those who litter the shoreline with glass, invariably raise my hackles, but somehow this message disarmed me. Its style was direct and unaffected, there was nothing cringing or subservient about it, and it exuded a manly independence characteristic of the wide-awake youngsters that Horatio Alger and Oliver Optic used to portray. I therefore pocketed the note—figuratively, that is, since I wore only bathing trunks—and later in the day complied with Donald's request. After recounting how it had reached me, I felicitated him on his vigorous, clean-cut rhetoric and his astuteness in modeling himself on such masters of English prose as Hazlitt and Defoe. Lest his ego become inflated, however, I hastened to point out that his handwriting was sorely deficient. "You will forgive me if I speak quite bluntly, my boy," I wrote, "but this progressive-school script of yours demeans you. I cannot stress too strongly the importance of good calligraphy in molding your future. A firm business hand with well-shaped capitals is a prerequisite in every field, be it the counting house, a mercantile establishment, or a profession like law or medicine. I suggest, accordingly, that you proceed with all dispatch to perfect yourself in the exercise known as Hammond arm movement, keeping the wrist flexible at all times and practicing the letter 'l' lying on its side."

As I weighed the foregoing prior to sealing the letter,

it struck me that a few words of counsel to the lad on his reading would not be amiss. I recommended, hence, that he familiarize himself with all the works of Henty, with the stories of Harry Castlemon (*Frank Before Vicksburg*, *Frank on a Gunboat*, etc.), with Ralph Henry Barbour's *Around the End*, and with anything by Altsheler he could find. He might also browse through the files of Hearst's *American Weekly* with profit, I added, quoting examples of the curious lore to be found there—the *S.S. Vaterland* posed vertically against the Singer Building to contrast their size, the eye of the common housefly magnified a hundredfold, the milk baths and other beauty secrets of Lina Cavalieri and Gaby Deslys, the advice on physical fitness from Jess Willard, and the disclosures about high society's Four Hundred by Count Boni de Castellane. In closing, I extended warm wishes and urged him to put his best foot forward, his shoulder to the wheel, and his nose to the grindstone—a pose guaranteed to excite the compassion of influential folk who might help him in his career.

I had quite forgotten the episode when, a month later in New York, I received a letter from a Mrs. Rhonda Cropsey. Writing on the stationery of a midtown hotel, she identified herself as Donald's mother and thanked me effusively for my epistle. She had taken the liberty of opening it, inasmuch as her son was in El Moribundo, California, visiting his father, from whom she was estranged. So brilliant, so truly inspired was my letter that before forwarding it she had made a copy, which she reread daily until every syllable was engraved on her heart.

"What a wonderful person you must be," she went

on. "A kind of saint, I imagine. Who else would trouble to reply to a child they didn't know, or bother to outline a program of studies to enlarge the little fellow's horizon? Never in all my twenty-eight years—yes, I am that young, even if I sound like an old fuddy-duddy—have I felt such gratitude to an individual. I really would do anything to reward them....But here I am wasting your valuable time with my silly-billy compliments; I guess I just can't help 'fessing up to hero worship if I feel same. Anyway, the reason for my contacting you at present is that I am in your bailiwick a day or two shopping for some feminine 'frillies' and wonder could we meet for five minutes to discuss little Don's next educational step. Won't you ring me very soon, pretty please?"

Well, that put me on the spot for fair. Here was a doting mama, undoubtedly a frump from backwoods Ohio, thirsting to talk me deaf, dumb, and blind about her precious darling, and yet to ignore her appeal would be tantamount to a slap in the face. I stewed over the problem for a good ten minutes and finally had an inspiration. I'd humor the woman and phone, but avoid any confrontation, wheedle or coax me though she might.

"Hello?...Yes, this is Rhonda Cropsey." The voice wasn't at all what I'd expected. It was low-pitched and cool, and there was a delicious tremor in it that made one's spine tingle. "O-oh, can it really be *you*?"

"Who else?" I stammered. "I mean—hello. Yes, it's me. Look—er—I've just had a cancellation. I'm terribly busy as a rule, but I could be at some central point like the Plaza bar in half an hour, if that's not inconvenient for you."

Not in the least, she quickly assured me—that would be ideal. I then gave her painstaking, explicit instructions as to which bar I meant, in case she blundered into the Palm Court or the Edwardian Room. Actually, my fears were groundless; far from a flibbertigibbet, Mrs. Cropsey proved to be not only alert but a demure and strikingly attractive young matron. If her figure was a shade too sensual for true beauty, it was compensated for by features that some Pre-Raphaelite painter—Burne-Jones or Dante Gabriel Rossetti—might have limned. Under a wealth of corn-colored hair worn in a snood, a pair of blue eyes looked out at the world with such trustful innocence that it wrung your heart. Her lack of sophistication became further evident when I asked what beverage she fancied.

"I-I've never tasted anything stronger than fruit juice," she confessed shamefacedly. "That cocktail you're having—a sidecar—what is it?"

I explained it was a mild digestive, compounded of the merest trace of brandy and a drop of Cointreau, and, reassured, she ordered one also. In a few moments our initial constraint had vanished and we were chatting away like old friends. It seemed hardly possible, I remarked, that one so girlish could have a twelve-year-old son, and she was equally incredulous at my laughing admission that I was past thirty. From the wisdom, the magnanimity implicit in my letter to Donald, she was prepared for a man twice, if not thrice, my years.

"Gracious, what a difference between you and that husband of mine!" she murmured, a shadow of pain contorting her lovely forehead. "Do you know that that swine used to beat me black and blue?"

Since I had never laid eyes on the swine in question, I felt ill-equipped to pass judgment, so, limiting my reaction to a pitying headshake, I ordered another round of drinks and deftly steered the conversation to her son. Precisely what advice did she seek from me about his schooling? A guilty blush suffused Mrs. Cropsey's cheek, and she hung her head penitently. Concerned as she was for the boy's welfare, she admitted to an ulterior motive in approaching me. She had tentatively selected a number of frocks, suits, and coats at a Fifth Avenue store and wanted me, her sole friend in New York and a man of faultless discrimination and taste, to choose the most becoming from among them. She realized it was a dreadful imposition, she was already indebted to me beyond measure, but this one final boon would forever enshrine me in her affections, elevate me to Olympus....In vain I protested my inadequacy to judge feminine fashions; the more vehement I grew, the more insistent she became, and at last, succumbing to a mixture of cajolery and sidecars, I broke down and assented.

In actual fact, the decisions Mrs. Cropsey exacted of me turned out to be trifling enough. I ran my eye expertly over the garments she was considering, compared various details of design and workmanship, and unerringly chose the best. The salesladies were frankly awed at my acumen, doubtless supposing that I was some biggie from the garment center. So harmonious was the atmosphere and so obliging the staff that my companion bought a few other articles— an expensive negligee, a couple of imported handbags, six pairs of shoes, and some diamond clips suitable for sports-wear. At her request, and for a bumper fee, all the purchases were dispatched by messenger to her hotel, and a floorwalker, rubbing his hands and bowing obsequiously, escorted us to the credit office, where she was to make payment. Suddenly, as she was rummaging in her bag, she emitted a startled exclamation. "My traveler's checks!" she gasped. "They're gone—they've been stolen! No—no—wait! I remember now—I left them behind at the hotel."

Drumming his fingers on the desk top, Seamus Mandamus, my lawyer, regarded me fixedly for several seconds over his glasses. "I see," he said with infinite sympathy. "So you helped her out, I take it. You wrote a check for the amount and then returned to her hotel so she could reimburse you."

I stared at him nonplussed. "How did you know?"

"Oh, just instinct." His smile radiated sheer benevolence. "Now, let me guess. When you got there, Mrs. Cropsey remembered something else. She *hadn't* left her checks in the hotel safe, as she thought at first, but in her room. So you accompanied her upstairs—right?"

"It wasn't a room—it was a suite," I corrected. "She had a living room with a pantry, a bedroom—"

"Yes, yes, I know what a suite is," he said impatiently. "Anyhow, there was a fifth of Scotch and some ice in the pantry, so she invited you to fix a drink while she went into the bedroom to fetch the checks."

"This is uncanny!" I exclaimed. "I swear, you sound as though you'd been there the whole time."

"If I had, Buster, you wouldn't be sitting here now with an ashen face," he rejoined. "One minor point, though. How did you reconcile the bottle of hooch with the lady's earlier statement that she never drank anything stronger than fruit juice?"

"Why—uh—it didn't occur to me," I said. "I may have been a little fuzzy from the sidecars."

"And the strain of shopping and all." He nodded beningnly. "But I imagine the fuzziness evaporated pronto when Mrs. Cropsey reappeared, eh? Weren't you startled that she had slipped into something more comfortable—something clinging and filmy?"

"Great, Scott, man, you must be clairvoyant!" I marveled. "Matter of fact, I *was* bowled over. But then, on top of everything, before I could catch my breath, those two hooligans with the camera burst in. There was this blinding flash—"

"You needn't go on," he interrupted. "It's cut and dried, a standard procedure. Did the fair one break into hysterical sobs after they left and lock herself in the bedroom?"

"You took the words out of my mouth," I said. "I hammered on the door for over half an hour, but not a tumble did I get. That was the last of Rhonda Cropsey."

"Not quite," replied Mandamus gently. "In case you still don't know the score, it becomes my painful duty to enlighten you. You are currently a co-respondent in the divorce action of Cropsey *v.* Cropsey, and a large, angry department store whose check you stopped is suing you for eleven hundred and eighty-five dollars in merchandise. I wonder whether you've learned anything from this experience."

I certainly had, though I wouldn't admit it to *that* shyster. The next time I see a bottle on a beach—or anywhere else—I intend to compress my lips in a thin line and kick it out of my path. And that goes for all twelve-year-old brats on the Nantucket boat and their blasted mothers.

Five Little Biceps and How They Flew

ALLERGY TO WORK IS REPORTED

CARAMANICO, *Italy (Reuters)—Some people are literally allergic to work, according to a report submitted to an Italian medical conference here. The report said that muscular activity could release an excessive amount of histamine, a powerful chemical stimulant in the body tissues, to cause rashes and allergies.*—The Times

HOUSTON, Tex. *(AP)—An Illinois psychiatrist says this country is being swept by an epidemic of work addiction. Dr. Nelson J. Bradley said work addiction has all the characteristics of alcohol or narcotics addiction.... The work addict has a driven craving for work, develops an increasing tolerance for it and suffers withdrawal symptoms without it, Bradley said. He said one sure sign of the work addict is habitually working overtime. He said another likely one is the man who says he has not taken a vacation in 17 years.*—New York Post

It was the kind of Pennsylvania Dutch barn immortalized by Andrew Wyeth and Charles Sheeler, a soaring nave of fieldstone to which various wooden transepts—a wagon shed, a granary, a forechute, and a silo had been added across the past century and a half, and every time I drove up our lane the sight of it dominating the ridge and the adjacent fields gave me a renewed sense of stability and peace. While wholly ornamental nowadays—a receptacle for firewood, discarded bookcases, and rusting pickaxes—it symbolized continuity, and the hex signs on the façade were a placatory gesture to destiny that was highly comforting. During the last couple of winters, however, time and the weather had made visible inroads. The paint had flaked off most of the siding, patches of stucco were missing from the gables, and overnight the picturesque had suddenly grown shabby. When a gossipy neighbor stopped me in the post office to observe with acid sweetness, "I hate to see the old landmarks disappear," I knew the community was buzzing. The barn had to be painted—sixty-five mortal gallons, I remembered from the past—and it was fruitless to sulk. I went in search of a contractor.

Mr. Trautwein, universally recommended as a wizard in his profession, lived thirty miles distant in a trim Mennonite hamlet in the back country. The houses flanking his glistened with fresh paint; their shutters glowed like cut velvet, their porches sparkled. Trautwein's residence, in distinction, was the most neglected dwelling I had seen outside the Gorbals in Glasgow. No trace of pigment showed on the weathered clapboards, the gutters sagged dispiritedly from the roof, and the yard was littered with turpentine cans, splintered glass, drop cloths, and similar detritus. Dismayed by these portents, I was about to clear off, but, recollecting the axiom that cobblers' children traditionally go unshod, I decided to persevere. Trautwein, a needle-nosed citizen with a Chester Conklin mustache, was immersed in a TV western he reckoned would occupy him for the remainder of the week, but he finally consented to drive over in a day or two and give me an estimate. With the instinctive timing of countryfolk, he materialized one evening just as my wife was extracting a soufflé from the oven, and the atmosphere when I bolted off to inspect the barn with him became abruptly charged. Trautwein's face lengthened at the magnitude of the task confronting him.

"Too far gone," he said gloomily. "Them boards'll suck up paint like a sponge. If I was in your shoes, I'd pull the durn thing down and use the wood for kindling."

I rejoined somewhat loftily that I had not been appointed chief minister of this domain to preside at the dissolution of my barn. The reference was clearly lost on him.

"Okeydoke," he said indifferently. "It's your money, not mine. You want a spray job or do we brush her on?"

"Hand work," I said, my voice resonant with admonitions gleaned from the *Consumers' Guide*. "The old-fashioned, painstaking way. Coat every nook, every knot with the best stuff obtainable, and damn the expense. This building was here when the red man roamed those woods, brother, and, by Godfreys," I vowed emotionally, "it'll be here when he returns!"

Assuring me that the mandate was graven on his heart, Trautwein took off, and a month passed without any word from him. I phoned his home half a dozen times, on each occasion falling into long, frustrating causeries with what were either children or chimpanzees; possibly both were being reared together as an experiment. Ultimately I cornered the man, only to be bombarded with excuses. The weather was too humid to paint and the insects too numerous, there was a nationwide shortage of ladders, and arthritis was epidemic among his help.

One August morning, long after my hopes had faded, a panel truck bearing no identification, like those used to merchandise hot furs, drew up at the corral and discharged two persons in white boiler suits and matching berets. My first supposition, that they were Andrew Wyeth and Charles Sheeler, yielded when they disclose themselves as emissaries of Trautwein—Russell Mulch and Howard Compost by name. As they started off-loading their gear, I was immediately struck by the difference between them. Compost's vigor was well-nigh manic; he whisked up five hogsheads of paint at once, threw scaffolding about like jackstraws, and flung a block and tackle with such force that it defoliated half the nasturtiums in our dory. Mulch, contrariwise, seemed to be tottering on the brink of invalidism, a pallid lymphatic shade whose every step threatened to be his last. Watching him struggle to open a can of putty, beads of perspiration the size of Catawba grapes dewing his forehead, I was appalled. To anyone with a professional eye like mine—and, as a onetime premedical student, I knew my way around pathology—the man was suffering from iron-poor blood. He was a gone goose.

At the moment, however, I had other matters

engaging my attention—notably, dipping sprays of Queen Anne's lace in whitewash to make floral arrangements for our hall—so I exacted a pledge from the duo to preserve the fine old Pennsylyania Dutch flavor of the barn and withdrew. An hour or two later, it proving unfeasible to watch them through field glasses from our bedroom, I sauntered out to investigate. Compost, in a display of almost inhuman energy, had singlehandedly primed two-thirds of the exterior, nailed fast all the battens, replaced the corrugated iron on the silo, given the hardware an undercoat of red oxide, and now straddled the roof in suicidal fashion, batting away pigeons as he daubed the crevices in the forepeak. His partner, Mulch, was nowhere in evidence, and, horrid as the surmise was, I wondered whether he had crept off into the fields to die. My fears were shortly assuaged; he was stretched out in our hammock under the maples, sneezing convulsively and disfigured by angry red blotches.

"Touch of ragweed, eh?" I said, expertly sizing up the dilated pupils and the flaccid wrists. "Still, it could be the shellac fumes—I recall some mention of that by my preceptor in pharmacology class. Well, stiff upper lip—we'll soon set you right."

I compounded a weak solution of bicarbonate, sirup of figs, and Dijon mustard—which I would have preferred to administer intravenously, but pulse and respiration (my own, that is) dictated otherwise—and he managed to ingest it. Distressing to report, his symptoms persisted; and I was thoroughly nonplussed by the time Trautwein appeared at dusk to check on his workmen. He betrayed marked evasiveness at my queries about Mulch, but eventually unbosomed himself. The man was totally allergic to work; if he so much as picked up a brush, in fact, wave after wave of histamine surged through his system, utterly devitalizing him.

"It happens on every job," he confessed. "Sometimes he can't even get out of the truck, poor bastard. It's the exact opposite with Howard, though." He pointed up at the ridgepole, where Compost was balanced like Bird Millman, frenziedly smearing away at his perch in the half darkness. "Now, him, he's liable to go on all night. I wouldn't dare stop him, else he'd come down with withdrawal pangs. You got to know how to handle these fellows."

"Well, I'll tell you one way," I suggested. "Why don't you put on *two* work addicts? They'd finish the chore in half the time."

"You mean, leave Russell go?" he asked incredulously.

"Er—only temporarily, until the job is finished," I said. "Fair is fair, but to pay someone for lounging in a hammock—"

Trautwein's lips tightened. "I ought to report you to the authorities," he said, outraged. "Aren't you ashamed, preventing a man from working just because his tissues are sensitive? He's got dependents, little kiddies that you're taking the bread out of their mouths. I never heard anything so heartless."

I was tempted to point out that if the kiddies, like his own, were hanging on the phone giving out misinformation, they were too busy to eat, but I forbore. At length, we hit on a *modus vivendi*; Compost would be asked to paint with two brushes to compensate for his colleague, the other's wages to be reduced by half. It was an equitable solution, and one, I felt, that would enable us to dwell together in harmony.

An hour before daylight next morning the dogs set up a hideous brouhaha. Compost had driven in, trained a searchlight on the barn, and, to the accompaniment of the "Washington Post March," was scraping the accumulated rust from the spouting. Mulch, on the other hand, failed to surface until eleven. After a few nerveless brushstrokes, he fell head foremost into the hollyhocks and had to be transferred to the screened porch, on which I could supervise his temperature more closely and supply him with barley water and magazines. As a small token of appreciation for Compost's zeal, my wife made up a picnic basket containing a block of foie gras, a Cornish hen, and an excellent Mâcon, but the gesture was futile; he insisted on working through lunch. His partner, though, got down the collation, and, indeed, revived sufficiently to sip a *vieux marc* and smoke a cigar. Improvising a sphygmomanometer from a bicycle pump and the gauge off an old hot-water heater—we medical people are trained to use the materials at hand—I took his blood pressure and found it encouraging. We were not out of the woods yet, but, provided Mulch had plenty of rest and never lifted a finger again, there was every indication he would pull through.

The picture up at the barn, however, was less reassuring. By nightfall Compost's exertions, far from slackening, had redoubled; temporarily forswearing his brush, he had hauled aloft half an acre of slate and was patching the roof. At ten-thirty, as my wife and I sat before Pandora's box, grinding our teeth at Susskind's euphuisms, it suddenly dawned on me that the chap had labored seventeen hours without surcease. My conscience rebelled and I jumped to my feet.

"Who the deuce are we—Simon Legree?" I exclaimed. "Folks'll drive by and see him up there, with the bats squeaking around—I'm stopping him this minute!"

"Are you out of your senses?" she asked, paling. "The fellow's hooked—you break it off and he'll go right into shock! And the next thing you know, you'll have a million-dollar lawsuit on your hands."

Though the woman's conception of immunology was primitive, there was no denying she had a certain legal instinct. In whatever case, the issue was resolved for us the very next day. Neither Compost nor Mulch showed up, and the place was as deserted as the Hadramaut. I let twenty-four hours elapse and began phoning Trautwein again, with the usual baffling results. Eons later he called back. Mulch had suffered a relapse while wielding a toothpick and was in traction.

"But where's Howard Compost? He's the one that matters," I expostulated.

"Oh, that two-timer," he said wrathfully. "I fired him. He was moonlighting between you and a job in Perkasie. But don't worry—your barn'll get done in a jiffy. I'm bringing over three crackerjacks bright and early tomorrow."

He was as good as his word. Hardly had I finished spraying the antrums for rose fever, oat fly, and horse dander—my own membranes are pretty delicate, but I don't beat my breast about it—when Trautwein roared up in his shooting brake and threw down the tailgate.

Out sprang a trio of needle-nosed youngsters easily identifiable as his—the eldest of them seven. Whooping and brandishing their brushes, they swarmed over the building like the followers of the Mahdi at Khartoum, but they delivered the goods, all right. There are those in the neighborhood, I hear, who claim the thing looks like a finger painting. Well, I should worry, I should fret, I should marry a suffragette. It sheds water, which is a hell of a lot more than you can say for most of your quaint old Pennsylvania Dutch barns.

Moonstruck at Sunset

I believe it was Hippolyte Taine, the historian—or possibly Monroe Taine, the tailor, a philosophical chap who used to press my pants forty years ago in the Village—who once observed that immortality is a chancy matter, subject to the caprice of the unborn. Not every notable wins his niche in the hall of fame on precisely the terms he would have chosen, and for every marbled dignitary in the Borghese Gardens or the Bois de Boulogne there is another who survives only as the trademark of a cigar, an italicized entry on a menu. Could Dickens have visualized himself as the patron saint of a taproom on West Tenth Street, or Van Gogh as the tutelary god of an Eighth Avenue cleaning establishment? Neither Dame Nellie Melba nor Lily Langtry, certainly, would have been content to face posterity as they have, one as a dessert and the other as a foundation garment. Perhaps the most eccentric parlay of this kind I know of, though, was unwittingly generated in the brain of a British novelist named Robert Hichens. When he spun his famous tale of Domini Enfilden's desert love and entitled it *The Garden of Allah*, he never could have foreseen the

299

landmark by that name—or, worse yet, a punning version of it—that would rise one day in Hollywood to perpetuate the glory of a Russian actress.

The actress, of course, was Alla Nazimova, and in naming a cluster of hotel bungalows on Sunset Boulevard the Garden of Allah the builder paid impressive tribute to her talent. (Since the builder happened to be Nazimova herself, there was never any question of her sincerity. With the passage of time, unfortunately, Nazimova's reputation waned and the Islamic cognomen prevailed.) As Hollywood architecture went, the place was fairly restrained—a sprinkle of tile-roofed, Neo-Spanish villas centered about a free-form pool—and its clientele equally so. Most of the hotel's guests were migratory actors, playwrights, and similar gypsies with tenuous links to the picture business, and if they reveled, they did so discreetly and in whispers. This was a source of perplexity to the press, notably a Manhattan columnist I once encountered on the grounds. It was his conviction that debauchery was mother's milk to screen folk, and he had selected the Garden of Allah as a vantage point to study it. Unable to find any orgies, he became morose, drank an immoderate amount of whiskey one night, and dove headlong into the pool in his dinner clothes. After his return to the East, he wrote a description of a couple of saturnalias he had attended in the Garden which would have shocked Petronius out of his toga.

The time was 1931, and my wife and I were recent arrivals in Hollywood, unfamiliar with its mores and domiciled in a sleazy bungalow court near the studio where I was undergoing my novitiate as a screenwriter. Our flat was less a home than a bivouac. The walls were plasterboard, the pastel-tinted furniture the flimsy type found in nurseries, the rugs and draperies tawdry, and the kitchenware minimal. As for the conversation of our fellow residents that filtered through the walls, that also promoted no feeling of stability. They seemed to be constantly staving off bill collectors and betting on horses that never finished, exchanging symptoms of these incurable diseases and rehearsing roles inevitably excised from films in the cutting room. But the rent was nominal and our discomfort somewhat allayed by the usual will-o'-the-wisp delusion that we were saving money hand over fist.

One evening I came home to find my wife dissolved in tears. After crystallizing her over a Bunsen burner, I managed to elicit the reason. A matron in Beverly Hills whom she knew had visited the premises that afternoon and pronounced them sordid. Ostracism, swift and pitiless, loomed in Filmdom unless we moved at once, her friend declared; the only possible locale that might restore the face we had lost was the Garden of Allah. I spurned the idea with such vehemence that the neighbors beat on the walls to quiet me, but their protests went for naught. In rhetoric that must have reminded them of Edmund Burke denouncing Warren Hastings, I poured vials of wrath on suburban snobbery; I blasted the colony's *nouveaux riches* until the welkin rang. When its strains died away, I realized the futility of argument and meekly started packing.

Since all the villas at the Garden were chockablock at the moment, we were lodged for an interval in a two-story annex overlooking the pool. The prospect from our windows was a soothing one—barbered lawns and shrubbery, emerald water rippling in the balmy California sunshine, and over all a genteel hush that bespoke affluence and contempt for vulgar display. Guests were rarely visible on the walks; occasionally a seamed old plutocrat in canary-yellow slacks doddered forth to exercise a Pekingese, or a European movie director in overtight satin shorts, mistakenly believing himself on the Riviera, would dog-paddle cumbrously about the pool, but otherwise the drowsy, peaceful scene was seldom marred. The first intimation of anything unusual came the second night after our arrival. Fire broke out in an apartment house nearby whose name immortalized still another celebrity—the Voltaire Arms—and some two dozen occupants of the Garden converged excitedly on the grass to watch. Among them were several screen personalities of both sexes whom we had no trouble identifying, as well as a number of prominent playwrights, executives, and agents. They were all officially married, but not to their present roommates. While startling, there was nothing indecorous about the assemblage; its members looked like sleepy children as they stood knuckling their eyes and gaping at the fire engines. One wondered if their faces would reflect the same dewy innocence in the divorce court.

Once ensconced in a villa of our own, it soon became evident that our neighbors, if more solvent than those in the bungalow court, were as peculiar. The man next door, for example, was a wizened homunculus who had edited one of the New York tabloids during the Peaches Browning era. Behind the smoked glasses that hid his saffron-colored face his eyes were on continual alert for some unseen enemy. I thought that perhaps he feared reprisals from gangland chiefs he had exposed, for he never ventured out except in a polo coat with upturned collar, and then only a few steps from his burrow. The explanation given my wife by our maid was more mundane: he was beset by process servers trying to collect the alimony he owed five women. His misogyny one day bore fruit. He wrote a book chronicling his vicissitudes, a best seller that became a hit play and eventually a musical smash—but his wives triumphed. They garnisheed his royalties, and he ended his days a bankrupt on a New Jersey goat farm.

In the cottage adjoining his was another enigma, a celebrated character actor whose behavior also occasioned intense speculation. A suave, courtly leading man popular on Broadway and in films, he was married to a society beauty no less distinguished than himself. Always arm in arm and solicitous of each other, they seemed a devoted couple, except that she often appeared in public with a black eye. He and I developed a nodding acquaintance, and one afternoon, quite without prompting, he confided to me that his wife had fallen the night before and struck her eye on a birdbath. A few days later she exhibited another shiner, contracted, he told me, in the same manner. The third time it happened I was tactless enough to ask if there was a birdbath in their villa, as I had seen none on the grounds. Our friendship curdled abruptly, which may have been providential. There were probably more black eyes where his wife's had come from.

Gradually, as time wore on, other transients whose actions defied analysis passed through the Garden—a gray-haired poetess who strummed a lyre outside her door for inspiration while composing her verses, a nautical couple who hung out a mess flag whenever they dined, and an Englishman who owned what appeared to be a haunted Rolls-Royce. The car, a vintage model, persisted in rolling out of the garage with nobody at the wheel—a habit he vainly sought to curb by keeping chocks under it and tying the gearshift with clothesline. It was obviously no easy task to minister to the whims of such diverse folk, and how Virgil, the hotel's one-man staff, accomplished it I could never understand. A stoop-shouldered, overworked wraith with an air of patient resignation like that of Zasu Pitts, he doubled as clerk, bellhop, and Florence Nightingale, forever in transit to Schwab's drugstore to fetch midnight sandwiches for the tenants, searching out bootleggers to allay their thirst, and nursing them through their subsequent hangovers. Whatever the commodity or service one demanded, whether it was caviar, a seamstress, bookends, or a massage, Virgil was the genie who supplied it, and after repeated demonstrations of his resourcefulness we began to regard him as superhuman. I found out otherwise when, yielding to his incessant entreaties, I bought two tickets to a spectacle called *The Love Life of Dorian Gray,* an amateur production then current at a neighborhood theater. The play was a fearful hash of epigrams torn out of context from the novel and refurbished with homemade apothegms such as "Love is like a lobster trap; those who are in wish to be out, and those who are out wish to be in." It was acted with unbearable elegance by a cast of heavily peroxided young men and one ill-favored girl, who clearly had backed the venture. Such was the lethargy it induced that by the final curtain all five of us in the audience—two drunken sailors, a nine-year-old boy, and ourselves—were petrified in our seats, unable to move. In the light of what ensued, though, I have to admit that the evening was not entirely wasted. The leading man, ranging the rest of the company before the footlights, requested our attention. "Ladies and gentlemen," he said earnestly, "exactly fifty-three years, six weeks, and four days ago, a traveler arrived at customs in New York who, when asked what he had to declare, responded, 'I have nothing to declare except my genius.' May I therefore ask you, my friends, to bow your heads along with ours in one minute of homage to a great playwright and a gallant gentleman—Oscar Wilde."

Though my horoscope failed to reveal that we were destined to revisit the Garden of Allah often in the following decade, one episode in that first tenancy remains forever etched on my memory. The film script I was crocheting at Paramount was a vehicle for a quartet of buffoons whose private lives were as bourgeois as their behavior on the screen was unbridled. Their actual identity is unimportant, but for those who insist on solving puzzles the ringleader of the group affected a sizable painted mustache and a cigar, and his three henchmen impersonated, respectively, a mute harpist afflicted with satyriasis, a larcenous Italian, and a jaunty young cox-comb who carried the love interest. Having supped repeatedly at the homes of all four, my spouse felt obliged to reply in kind, and, in an ill-considered burst of generosity, invited them and their wives to dinner at the Garden. "We'll have drinks and canapés in our place beforehand," she informed me, "and then take them over

to the dining room." Overriding my protest that it was a
catacomb, she said, "Yes, yes, I know how depressing it is,
but Virgil's promised to put in two more forty-watt
bulbs, and, anyway, they'll have such a skinful by then
that they won't know what they're eating."

"OK, but that's only half the problem," I said. "How
about the dog?" We had a fairly unruly pet at the time, a
standard schnauzer who ate everything he could get his
paws on. "He's never seen people like these—I better
keep him locked up in the bedroom so he doesn't bite
one of them. After all, they're my livelihood."

Deriding me as a Cassandra and a calamity howler,
she went ahead with her preparations, ordering flowers
and liquor as lavishly as if for a wedding and mailing
elaborate reminder notes to the members of the troupe.
On the appointed evening they appeared with their
wives, the latter exhibiting noticeably sullen faces. I was
not aware then of something I learned much later—that
these kinswomen were at daggers drawn and never saw
each other socially. While the men stood around glumly
draining their cocktails, the ladies began exchanging
barbs so venomous that I was afraid homicide might
follow.

"I *love* your hat, darling," one complimented another
who was wearing a cloche composed entirely of feathers.
"You know something? It makes you look exactly like a
little brown hen."

"You don't say," her sister-in-law replied sweetly.
"Well, it's a long time since anyone called *you* a chicken."

As the tension mounted and the atmosphere became
charged, I grew panic-stricken, and I may have mixed
stronger drinks for the company than was prudent. At

any rate, I, for one, was sufficiently expansive by the time we were midway through dinner to nourish the illusion that the party was a roaring success. In my relief at having averted mayhem, it mattered not that the food was inedible, the service appalling; I skipped about in the murk lightheartedly refilling everyone's wineglass, joshing the men and charming the ladies—I was, in a word, the perfect host. Indeed, my gaiety was so infectious that the assemblage sat there openmouthed, whether in wonder or overcome by yawns it was too dark to determine. Finally, however, my cornucopia of badinage and jollification was emptied, and the guests trooped back to our villa to retrieve their wraps. I strode ahead of them, giving my version of Richard Tauber interpreting the "Song of the Volga Boatmen" and, as I threw open the door, was confronted by a startling tableau: Cradled in the mink coat that belonged to Mustachio's wife lay our schnauzer, with an object I dimly recognized as her cloche bonnet between his forefeet. He had just stripped the very last feather from its surface and was smirking at us with the pride of an artisan whose work is well done.

Gone is the Garden today, and on its site there stands a curious structure that is either a bank housing an art gallery or an art gallery housing a bank—in Hollywood one never knows. Nowhere inside, though, will the cinema buff find a plaque or any clue to commemorate the shrine a Russian tragedienne erected to herself, and yet none is really necessary. Whenever I traverse Sunset Boulevard nowadays (which, praise God, is hardly ever), I always stop and bow my head in one minute of homage to a great actress and a gallant real-estatenik—Alla Nazimova.

Hark—Whence Came Those Pear-Shaped Drones?

I say, would it be indiscreet of a married man to kiss and tell—to confess that the other day he found himself in the same boat with an appealing Englishwoman who stirred his senses? Oh, I can read your mind; you doubtless visualize a blissful pair out of an early Compton Mackenzie novel, drifting lazily downstream in a punt past the dreaming spires of Cambridge, with Cicely trailing the tip of her parasol in the lilies and I, Leslie Howard reborn in my immaculate flannels, poling our craft along and apostrophizing her with a verse of Robert Herrick's. (While all unbeknownst to us, a fanatical Serb in faraway Sarajevo prepares the coup that will end our golden dream forever.) Well, you're wrong—I was merely using a metaphor in a quite prosaic sense. I just meant that when I read a letter in the London *Times* from Mrs. Janet Barney of Pangbourne, Berkshire, appealing for help, my heart warmed toward her because I'd once been involved in a plight almost identical with hers. Mrs. Barney—whose letter, by the by, confirms her as a lovely person, the sort you actually would apostrophize—was imploring the women's page for advice on how to cope with girls imported from the Continent as mother's helpers. "I'd like to appeal to your more experienced readers," she wrote, "for a set of simple rules for 'au pairs.' I'm not sure where I go wrong. I suspect it is my fault that the girls take more and more liberties. By the time they leave us, they are eating us out of house and home, staying out late, using all the bath water, borrowing the children's socks and disappearing when needed most. I do keep my end of the bargain with continuous English lessons, generous pocket money, trips out, special traditional dishes, and so on, but somehow I end up washing dishes while the au pair plays tennis with my racquet with my friends. Who will advise me before I spoil the next one?"

Though children played no part in my own predicament, the complications that arose from harboring two young foreigners paralleled Mrs. Barney's so strikingly that her words gave me gooseflesh. (Well, metaphorically.) I should explain that about a year ago I began to be concerned about the burden imposed on my wife by life in the country. Instead of playing Chopin on the pianoforte or painting skillful, evocative watercolors as I'd envisioned, she was busying herself with a score of menial tasks, as exhausting as they were unnecessary. She was forever upstairs and down, pushing a carpet sweeper into dark corners, suspending rolls of flypaper from the ceiling, polishing the isinglass in the coal stoves, and hoisting hundredweights of ice, which bade fair to slip out of the tongs and crush her foot into our icebox. In addition to whitewashing the hens—a chore whose value, to say the least, was arguable—she had started to fashion souvenir

S J Perelman

birchbark canoes as a source of pin money, as if the allowance I made her were not already lavish. It offended me that a woman of refinement and intellect, a bluestocking and a product of the best finishing schools, should expend her energy on such footling pursuits, and I said so in no uncertain terms. To my surprise—for I foresaw strenuous objections—she signified her readiness to abdicate at once if I could furnish another drudge.

"Now, wait a minute," I demurred. "Cleaning women don't grow on trees, you know, and they're not cheap. Some of them get as much as thirty-five cents an hour....What did you say?"

"Nothing," she said. "OK. How about a nice couple?"

"Honey," I protested. "It stands to reason that if one person earns thirty-five an hour, two would be twice as expensive."

"Well, then, we'd better look around for a robot," she snapped, with an abruptness that sounded like the slam of a zinc-lined icebox. "You don't expect anyone to work for free, do you?"

"Hold on—you may have thrown me into an idea," I said. "Why don't we spring for an *au pair*—a couple of European youngsters who'd appreciate a good home in the country, rambles galore, and the chance to brush up their English on our Linguaphone records?"

The prospect of supervising two immature aliens, to be truthful, dismayed her at first, but she finally capitulated, and I called an agency in New York specializing in placements of the sort. Ten days later I was notified that Denise Savoureux and Cosette Oscillant were arriving by bus at Trenton the following

310

noon, and I drove in to meet them. The moment the girls appeared in the terminal, a sensation overcame me as of one who has just put foot in a quicksand (*qui a posé son pied dans un sable mouvant*). Far from being adolescents, the two were young ladies whose conformation caused a perceptible stir at the gates; in fact, our introductions were well-nigh inaudible, due to wolf whistles in the background. Denise was a lush, green-eyed blonde of the type you see ogling sailors on sentimental French postcards, her companion a sultry brunette with a teasing smile that coiled itself around the male passerby like a boa constrictor. Accompanying me toward the exit in their pitiful miniskirts and blouses, the latter, plainly woven of cobwebs, they seemed to undulate rather than walk. A hot blush suffused my face, and I suddenly felt myself transported to Marseilles, a trafficker in the South American export trade. Rather than suntans and a madras shirt, I ought to be wearing a gooseneck sweater, a cap, and a quarter inch of Gaulois depending from my nether lip.

Luckily the illusion that I was Pope le Moko dissipated on our journey homeward, enabling me to correct a few misapprehensions about the girls. The agency's description of them as former students at the Sorbonne was fanciful; Denise had been a coatroom attendant at the Crazy Horse Saloon, on the Left Bank, and Cosette a manicurist in the barber shop of the Hotel Georges Cinq. In consequence, their English, which I had been led to understand was minimal, was far more fluent than mine, and much racier. It had improved as well under the tutelage of their first employer in America, a sportswriter on Long Island—a goatish character whose hands; they confided, smiling reminiscently, were always straying. And where had they worked thereafter, I inquired. Most recently in Las Vegas, in a Lido-type floor show at Caesar's Palace. Pleasant and cool though the ambience, their costumes consisting of no more than a handful of feathers, they much preferred a home environment like the one I was taking them to. I dummied up and said farewell to the brioches, croissants, and quiches Lorraine I had promised ourselves. How on earth was I going to install a ramp of the kind these babes wore accustomed to in our dining alcove?

My wife's reaction to Denise and Cosette was, at any rate heartening; if she felt either dizziness or an impulse to faint, she concealed it and behaved with signal worldliness and aplomb. She did, however, insist that they be lodged elsewhere than in the house, since, as she lightly explained, our proximity could easily degenerate into a French farce. She conducted the girls, accordingly, to guest quarters in an outbuilding a few yards distant, and, with the injunction to slip into something less comfortable than their peekaboo blouses, invited them to relax and familiarize themselves with the premises.

"They're awfully disappointed we haven't a pool," my wife disclosed in the kitchen as she set about preparing a traditional dish to make the two feel at home—a trout blue with almonds. "Maybe you should get a quotation on what it'd cost to put one in temporarily. Oh, yes, and while you're about it, find out about the barn—I think it would make an ideal casino. This place must be such a letdown after Vegas."

Hark—Whence Came Those Pear-Shaped Drones?

From the restraint shown toward the *pièce de résistance* and the significant glances her aides exchanged, it was clear Madame's cuisine had not swept them away. They displayed tolerance toward the wine, however, deeming a bottle of Beaune I had cherished for twenty years a decent enough vintage. In the hope they would assist with the dishes, I washed a few to acquaint them with the technique, but they retired yawning to the piazza and partook copiously of our Chartreuse. The television set having broken down some weeks earlier, we amused ourselves watching the fireflies. Cosette asked if there were any velodromes in the area, or a discothèque for young folk.

"There's a roller rink open Thursdays in French-town," my wife imparted. "Boys? Hm-m-m, not too many in this section. We have one who mows the grass, but he's just been here."

"Well, phone him to cut it again," said Denise, green eyes glinting like a leopard's on stalk. "*Mon Dieu,* listen to how quiet it is, Cosette. This place is a sepulcher."

The stillness prevailed only until the arrival next day of the milkman, who, after one glimpse of our charges, sped off to rouse the countryside. Within an hour the driveway was choked with vehicles of every description —pickups, tractors, sports cars, scooters, and buck-boards. Carpenters and plumbers we had vainly besought for years to make vital repairs swarmed over the place offering their services and undercutting each other's estimates. A truck appeared with Nards and Beck and Reedsworth Smiles, a trio of electricians eager to rewire the house at cost, and farmers who had spurned our fields for years as eroded and sterile clamored to replant them, pressing free seed on us. Amid the cataclysmic uproar Denise and Cosette held court in the kitchen, dispensing cokes by the dozen to their red-faced, perspiring swains and teaching them to dance the java. So distracting was the resultant pinching and squealing that I could abide it no longer and bore my wife off to a barbecue stand, where we could lunch in peace. The girls had taken French leave in our absence, but a note informed us that they had gone swimming in the Delaware, whose many eddies can be treacherous if there are no hands to pull one out. Apparently there were, for when they reached home at 3 A.M., the playful slaps and oo-la-la's that rang through the valley reassured us that they were still alive, if somewhat shopworn.

What with the black coffee, the Bromo-Seltzers, and the icebags their hangovers required that morning, it was small wonder my wife mistook me for Eric Blore miming a sympathetic manservant in an RKO musical, yet the eternal feminine in her would not be stilled; did I linger an extra moment in the guesthouse, she stalked in with arms akimbo and extricated me gently but firmly by the ear. Her casual suggestion to Cosette and Denise over breakfast that they help with the housework evoked only a sullen silence that persisted until two pustular youths materialized with a power boat on a trailer to escort them to the Jersey shore. In the ensuing three days we saw them hardly at all. They flew in sporadically to use the phone or to bathe—with, I may say, reckless disregard for towels, which cost us a mint to launder—and it was painfully apparent from their chill behavior that our attempt to befriend these petrels from an alien shore had failed. One evening, though, their mood seemed to have undergone a magical change; radiant with suppressed excitement, their eyes sparkled mischievously and giggles convulsed their abundant frames. Investigation revealed that our neighborhood art festival, an annual affair, was featuring a revue, the director of which had invited them to participate. It was a splendid opportunity to involve themselves in the artistic life of the community, and I approved wholeheartedly.

"What sort of specialty will you do?" I asked, glowing with pride that the family was to be represented. "Characteristic folk songs—*chansons* from Brittany and Provence? Or plaintive ballads, like those of Edith Piaf and Aznavour?"

"*Oui, oui—peut-être,*" they replied distractedly, and rushed off to rehearsals. Instinct told me that it was unwise to catechize them. They wanted freedom to choose their own creative outlet, to express themselves wholly and untrammeled. I respected that. It showed spunk.

It showed much more than that, as it developed. The spectacle attracted a capacity audience—the largest in years—which included many carpenters, plumbers, electricians, and farmers not normally patrons of the theater. We ourselves sponsored a party of friends prominent in the musical world and interested in the *lieder* the girls might sing. The setting of their act was an old-fashioned minstrel number performed by local teenagers, who rattled their tambourines with engaging professionalism as the end-men exchanged jokes about chicken stealing and wooden razors. When the mirth subsided, an orchestral flourish and roll on the snare drums brought our protégés weaving sinuously out of the wings. They wore deeply incised evening gowns threatening to burst at each breath, opera-length gloves, and aigrettes improvised from broom-straws in their hair. To the strains of "A Pretty Girl Is Like a Melody" the pair began a slow strip as calorific as Georgia Sothern's, interspersed with grinds and bumps that lashed their admirers to frenzy. Urged on by hysterical chanting, they had peeled down to G-strings and pasties and were preparing to discard those when a flying wedge from the ladies' auxiliary shot over the footlights and swept them offstage.

En route to the Trenton bus terminal early next day, Cosette expressed chagrin that our association had withered on the vine (*devenu jaune sur la vigne*). It always happened when there was a bossy woman around, Denise observed with a typically Gallic shrug; actually, they had longed to prepare me a few regional dishes like *cassoulets* and *ratatouille*, but what would you, the mistress of the house would have scratched out their eyes in jealousy. As I was stowing their luggage on the rack I overheard the driver agree to deposit them at an establishment outside Perth Amboy called the Diamond Bikini. I must stop by there sometime. It's probably the only roadhouse in New Jersey, if not the world, that can boast a couple of authentic, dyed-in-the-wool *au pair* girls.

Too Many Undies Spoil the Crix

My little gray home on West Forty-fifth Street, all six depressing floors of it, looked as tawdry as ever when the cab rolled up in front, but from halfway across the sidewalk a new appendage caught my eye. Bulging out of the fake-marble trim around the entrance was a stylish bronze plaque that read "Jampolski Arms" in low-relief script. Guzek, the super, had just finished buffing it with a chamois and was squinting at the result, a cigar stub clamped in his teeth.

"Say, what gives?" I asked. "Don't tell me the building changed hands while I was in Boston."

Guzek shrugged. "The owner's idea," he said. "He felt the joint needed more class."

"But who's Jampolski?" I said. "*His* name's Sigmund Rhomboid."

"It's his common-law wife," he said. "He picked it on account of she's got these lovely white arms."

The thought of the spongecake beneath Gotham's callous exterior, without a troubadour like Nick Kenny or Odd McIntyre around any longer to extoll it, brought a momentary lump to my throat, but I choked it back and went into the foyer. The usual accumulation of trash mail welcomed me—mournful appeals from atomic spies for a new trial, threats from Internal Revenue—along with the standard weekly bleat from Roxanne. Los Angeles was a cultural desert, our divorce had left her with migraine and permanent insomnia, and enclosed was a bill I had overlooked from I. Magnin's. To top everything off, the cleaning woman had neglected to dust my flat, owing, she explained in a note written in Linear B, to her brother's sudden demise in Richmond. Poor thing—that made the twelfth relative she had buried since Christmas. If her necrology was accurate, it surpassed anything outside Defoe's *The Journal of the Plague Year.*

I was hardly out of the shower before Ned Bluestone called. His voice was in the key of C, so anxiety-ridden that my receiver shook. Why hadn't I phoned him after the first Boston performance, wired him, contacted him on arrival? What kind of a press agent was it who disappeared for days on end? In all his experience as a producer—

With a sharp cry I cut short the familiar narrative of how he had risen from booking Bluestone's Merry Maids on the Poli circuit to Broadway eminence.

"What's wrong? What happened there?" he demanded.

"It's Mrs. Jampolski," I said breathlessly. "She just ran down the fire escape stark naked, followed by a man with goat's feet. I'll dig you later."

By the time I reached the office Bluestone had worked off some of his adrenalin on subordinates, an agent or two, and a few overseas calls, but he still twitched uncontrollably, and, with his greenish complexion, he could have doubled for a grasshopper in a Karel Capek fantasy. "Well, spill it, can't you?" he snapped. "What's the verdict? Have we got a show?"

"Ned," I said, "now that you're *bar mitzvah*, the gold watch you wear symbolizes a man's responsibilities. Gird yourself—it's a bomb."

"You didn't buy it," he said, with a true showman's instinct.

"I'll spell it out," I said. "There are some soporifics, like *The Sound of Music*, that lull the theatergoer. *Let's Skip Dinner* goes beyond that—it maddens. I don't want to alarm you, but the Broadway première of this play will be another Night of the Long Knives. They'll eviscerate you—hunt you down with dogs."

To my surprise he nodded somberly. "I knew it the minute I read the script. I hated it, but when that Mrs. Ample Hindquarters and her society jeweler, Sterling Flatware, offered to put up the scratch, I lost my judgment. Maybe if we sent for Abe Burrows—"

"Not a prayer," I said. "Believe me, no digitalis in his satchel or anybody else's can save this one. Close it, I beseech you."

"What, and sacrifice the parties I lined up?" He recoiled from the unclean thought. "Don't be an ignatz. We still got an out, and it's a blockbuster—a bold stroke of genius." He fumbled a clipping out of his desk. "Read that."

Headlined "Not So Tough," the item had been culled from a column of theater miscellany in the *News* under the byline of James Davis. It ran, "The Broadway critics who leave overcoats behind and spend intermissions outside the theater in comfort while others shiver aren't as rugged as they seem. One critic's valet told us they *all* wear two or three sets of underwear under their pants and jacket."

"Well, I've dealt with some devious minds in my time, but yours is the original Hampton Maze," I said perplexedly. "What's the point?"

"Schlemiel! Idiot! Don't you get it?" Bluestone crowed. "We bribe the respective valets to forget the extra underwear a few days before we open, and the critics all come down with colds and flu. So we draw the second-string reviewers, which are good-natured, kindly exponents of live and let live, not like these other vultures"

"Ned, it pains me to say this," I said. "You've swum away from the float. The strain of this production—"

"I figured it from every angle, and it can't miss," he said, his juggernaut careering over me. "The *Farmer's Almanac* predicts subzero temperatures the rest of the month. The shows preceding us, I'll get the managers to seat the critics near the doors, in a good strong draft. If necessary, we plant someone behind to sneeze on them. I guarantee the whole kit and caboodle's in bed with fever opening night."

Inured to show-biz hysteroids by long association, I realized the futility of argument. "Well, the whole thing sounds wacky to me," I said. "How the hell can Umlaut, on the *Times*, and Jack Chopnick, of the *News*, afford valets on their salaries?"

"Precisely!" said Bluestone joyously. "That's why they're vulnerable. Their manservants probably work for peanuts, and if you slip 'em a fin or so to overlook the extra union suits, why, it's pennies from heaven. Now, here's the names my girl wheedled out by pretending to be a *Time* researcher. Get busy, and walk on eggshells, for Crisake. This could be dynamite if it leaked."

Had Eric Ambler and Graham Greene linked arms with E. Phillips Oppenheim, they would have been stumped to invent the machinations I engaged in the following week. Under the guise of Sigmund Jampolski, proprietor of the Fragrant Hand Laundry, I called on the retainers in question—all of them English, as it developed—and earnestly solicited the household business. The prestige of handling such distinguished wash, I explained, was so great that I was prepared to do it for nothing—in fact, I offered them a bonus of twenty dollars apiece for the privilege. The alacrity they responded with convinced me that I could safely proceed to the second, and more delicate, stage of my plan. I invited each in turn, beginning with Yelverton, Umlaut's man, to have a drink. Our first encounter was purely social; I rhapsodized about Britain, feigned deep interest in their careers and problems, and did my utmost to cultivate rapport. At our next meeting I casually led the conversation around to their employers. I ventured that anyone who wore two or three suits of underwear, as the *News* had disclosed, must be a bit of a hypochondriac.

Yelverton's reaction, typical of the rest, was heartwarming. "A *bit?*" he echoed. "Why, Mr. Umlaut's absolutely bonkers on the subject of his health! Ah, Jampolski, nobody knows what I endure—the poultices, the croup kettles, the endless complaints about his aches and pains. Sheer imagination, of course."

"Arising from insecurity and his humble birth, doubtless," I said. "This may seem odd coming from a laundryman, Yelverton, but I majored in psychology at Loyola U., and there's only one way to cope with people like that. They must be deprived of their crutch—in this case, excess underwear. Why not restrict him to a single suit some evening?"

"Good Lord, I wouldn't dare," he said, taken aback. "What if he caught a chill on the liver?"

"Balderdash," I said forcefully. "The sudden knowledge that he was liberated from his neurosis would make him eternally grateful—he'd idolize you."

"We-ll-l-l, maybe." He looked dubious. "No valet is a hero to his man, you know."

"Unless he earns it," I said. "Tell you what, Yelverton. I'm so certain my theory's sound that I'll back it up with hard cash. Would a hundred dollars tempt you to try it?"

His face registered such bewilderment, tinged with suspicion, that I decided not to press him; I wanted the poison to circulate in his veins. Shortly afterward he phoned me with a counterproposal, which he found some hesitation in wording. A lady friend of his—his fiancée, really—had taken a fancy to a small diamond brooch in Lambert's priced at four hundred and thirty-five dollars. Did I regard it as a wise investment? You know more about psychology than I do, you muzzler, I thought, and asked him for time to consider.

When I called Bluestone to OK the expenditure, he screamed bloody murder. "What are we running—a soup kitchen?" he cried. "Offer him a cheap Swiss watch or something! My cousin in the jewelry center can get me a rakeoff."

"I'm having the same headache with Copestone, the bird who works for Wasservogel, on the *Post*," I said.

"He's holding out for a vicuña coat. And Rowntree; who looks after Zemel, on *Women's Wear*, gave me a song and dance about a sports car."

In the tirade that ensued I gathered Bluestone was about to call the DA's office and lodge charges of extortion, but when I succeeded in interjecting the word "boomerang," he subsided. I was empowered to go to two hundred dollars; anything more would be downright vampirism and deductible from my own stipend. As for the task of persuading the valets to synchronize their mischief on the same night, Bluestone took a magnanimous line. "Now, let's not try to butcher the whole gang," he counseled. "I don't want every single critic in bed with pneumonia—just enough so's we get a fair shake from the small fry. Immobilize the key people, but remember, don't offend anybody."

In the end, and after a prodigal outlay of flattery, liquor, and the minimum of cash, I managed to win over Yelverton, Copestone, and Clunes—the last, Chopnick's batman on the *News*. The role of Jampolski, meanwhile, was proving arduous; I was at my wit's end directing a corps of messengers to collect and deliver the critics' laundry. They were a carping lot, these gentlemen of the press, as quick to pounce on flaws in my work—the wrinkled cuff, the missing button—as those in the plays they appraised. Nevertheless, the fuse I had laid was ignited on schedule. The thermometer had dropped, my trio of cat's-paws had cut back on their employers' insulation, and *Let's Skip Dinner* was closing in Boston preparatory to the Broadway première when fate hurled a thunderbolt. Irving Cubbins, our male lead, inadvertently set fire to his toupee while smoking in bed at the Hotel

Touraine, sufficiently fricasseeing his scalp so that another zombie had to be flown in from the Coast. To allow the replacement time to get up in the part, Bluestone switched the production into Philadelphia for a week. The next morning he phoned me from the box office in a state bordering on delirium. The show had drawn rave notices, the most ecstatic in memory, and the ticket line was impeding traffic as far west as Valley Forge. All previous plans, consequently, were scrubbed; New York was to be a glittering first night, covered by strictly topflight critics capable of assaying a theatrical gem.

It was infanticide to puncture his balloon, but I had to tell him the truth. "The damage is done, Ned," I said. "It's too late. Umlaut's at Lenox Hill with laryngitis, Wasservogel was carried out of the Alvin last night with his eyes streaming, and Chopnick has either quinsy or whooping cough—his physician won't say."

"They can have cholera for all I care!" he bellowed. "You get those three to their chairs Tuesday night even if you have to use a stretcher. Tell the nurse to feed 'em orange juice, vitamins—call Michael DeBakey in, Texas for a free opinion!"

"You have but to command, *mon général*," I said dutifully, and hung up. I cleaned out my desk, took a cab to "21," and had a four-hour lunch with the prettiest girl I knew—a doll reminiscent of Aileen Pringle—at the end of which I somewhat expunged Bluestone's indignities by signing his name to a ninety-dollar check.

Let's Skip Dinner, sadly, didn't quite justify its producer's forecast as the hit of the century. The invective that greeted it in New York, in fact, would have dumfounded even a connoisseur like Hugh Kingsmill.

The second-string critics attended, clad in only one suit of underclothes, and voted it the most aptly initialed hallucinogen of the year, the deadliest blight to befall entertainment since *The Ladder*. Bluestone instantly vanished into television, where he was soon entrusted with the guidance of an entire network. When, six months later, I applied through an intermediary for a job in its press department, he turned to stone. "Don't mention that bastard's name to me," he groaned. "He was associated with one of my worst disasters."